Are We Here To Re-Create Ourselves?

◆ ◆ ◆

The Convergence of Designs

D0710919

By Geoffrey Simmons, M.D.

Dedicated to Paul Gossard, the best editor that a writer could have ever had. RIP. And, to my wife Sherry, a terrific partner, and to my uncle Lew (relatives don't come better). Thank you to our Designer whose Wisdom I constantly seek.

Table of Contents

"Imitation is the sincerest form of flattery."

CHARLES CALEB COLTON (1780-1832), ENGLISH CLERIC
AND WRITER

Introduction

If the theory of evolution is correct and life was created by a lightning strike plus trials-and-errors, mutations, accidents and natural selection, there is no inherent purpose for our presence on Earth. None. No more than fallen leaves on a roof or to dust on the floor. Life becomes what one makes it and/or what one is told. Whoever controls the reins, in a sense, whatever is discovered by science, and what may happen by serendipity, determines much of our destiny.

If an Intelligent Designer (ID) is responsible for our presence on Earth, it is reasonable to assume that there are many purposes for human life. These include pursuing happiness, helping others, knowing God, having dominion over Earth and its life forms, staying healthy and raising a family. Another, possible and more tangible reason, however has come to light recently. That is the re-creation of ourselves to improve our lives, expand our capabilities and safely travel within and beyond our solar system. With ID comes God-inspired and God-given rules.

The idea that life originated and/or was altered by visits from extraterrestrials, (also, a type of ID) albeit it entertaining and fanciful, remains unfounded.

Determining how we got here should help us understand where we are going and why. And, maybe even how. Nowadays, scientists can easily see the transition steps (those being macro, micro, sub-micro and molecular) that would be needed to change one species into another, such as a single cell organisms to multicellular organisms, reptiles into birds or monkeys into men and women; yet, these steps (links) are way too numerous, complex, fragile and convoluted to have simply come about by accidents or natural forces.

For the theory of evolution to ever be correct (and as is, it's not), it would have needed interventions or Intelligent Guidance at all levels. Albeit the appellation is sometimes conjured up to use in a derogatory sense, there had to have been interventions by a "God of the Gaps". That is, a Designer for the Gaps. Horses can be bred to run faster (up to a point), but they cannot be bred to become any other animal. Perhaps, there will be a thousand pure breeds of dogs, but every one, regardless of color, size, and talents, will remain dogs. A feathered dinosaur might have been able to fly, but a God of the Gaps must have taught it how to make a nest in a tree. The human clotting system has way too many converging pathways and steps to have happened without this God. The human brain has billions, if not trillions, of additions, since the first animals without intervention from this same God.

I hope to show how past converging designs by humans have led to present designs and how converging designs will carry us into the future. These patterns are readily apparent if one merely seeks them out. I also believe understanding humanoid design helps understand human and Intelligent Design(ID).

I believe that I would be remiss if I didn't give you some of my personal credentials from the outset and tell you where this book will take you.

I recently retired from practicing internal medicine, after forty-five years. My specialty deals with the anatomy, physiology, and a host of human vulnerabilities, from the teenage years to the end of life, through good and bad health, and how all of it all plays out for each of us.

Physicians, I believe, are among the best observers of life processes. Most people view the human body from the stratosphere. From that height, all aspects of life can seem relatively simple and easy to explain. If one were to drop down into the micro-world, however one would readily see that **nearly everything living is inexplicable.** Just watch a sperm entering an ovum, a fertilized egg changing into an embryo, billions of DNA segments directing cellular activities, thousands of genes sending out orders, thousands of RNA molecules carrying messages, the manufacture of tens of thousands of proteins, different kinds of white cells fighting side-by-side with antibodies to destroy microscopic invaders, uncountable numbers (quadrillions, perhaps) of bacteria helping intestinal cells breakdown and digest food, activated platelets plugging up hemorrhaging wounds and scar-forming tissues pulling wounds closed. Watch a single cell selectively absorb nutrients and water. These activities, and many like them, work tirelessly day and night to keep us going; they repair themselves on the run, modulate their activities, and replace themselves as needed. They are nearly timeless also, repeating generation after generation after generation.

All of the designs of life and how they came together to form a human being at the right time, in the right place and in the right way is also beyond understanding. There's more activity going on in a drop of blood than what's happening inside the world's largest skyscraper. Our lungs and heart are extremely compatible, as are all of our organs. Our hands match up as do our eyes, ears, and breasts. None of this is by luck or accident. Our brain functions better than millions of linked computers. Perhaps, billions. Also, not by good luck or accident.

There's more activity going on in the human body than in all of the major metropolitan areas of the world, combined. And, none of it is simple activity. Far from it. **There is, and has been, an incredible convergence of designs within a convergence of designs in everything we do, say, see, hear and think.** One readily sees this throughout Nature, past and present.

Most of us, I suspect, would like to know whether our presence here on Earth is accidental or purposeful. If we were are only here by accident, there is no apparent purpose for our being. Life might be whatever you make it. Yet, if there's a reason, meaning done on purpose by a (D)designer, it is each person's responsibility to ferret out those goals and strive to achieve them. With rare exceptions, I believe they are lofty.

I hope to give you an overview of a relatively new, yet (actually old), purpose. That is the re-creation of ourselves. To do so, I will make use of current theories regarding our reason for being here on Earth. I will show how our bodies are the consequence of converging designs. For example, the linking of a developing circulation system (a design) in a human fetus to the evolving heart portals (designs) and the linking of developing nerves (designs) in the spinal cord to the different muscle systems (designs). Not only was there micro-convergence beforehand, but there is macro-convergence now.

Perhaps, one can visualize this idea better when viewing the automobile industry. An evolving car requires the convergence of different designs: one or more for the chassis, engine, interior, seats, paint, steering column, steering wheel, brakes, tires, suspension system, lighting, AC and heat, windows, wipers, seabags and fuel management. An aircraft carrier requires many more converging designs. International space stations and eventual outposts on the moon and Mars will be another design dimension forward. Yet, all of manmade designs are pale by comparison to the design we see in the human being. We are made of designs within designs within designs, working in parallel, opposition and/or succession. That means incredible complexity piled upon incredible complexity. In a sense we are an enormous skein of origami.

The working title to this book was once *How to make a Human Being*, but I realized, while working on the last revision, something was missing. I needed something linking all of the parts. It was then that I realized that everything, whether it be technical or biological, was related to converging designs, too. Design can be found everywhere inside and outside our body from the shape of our nose to the form of a gene in a single cell. The chair you are sitting on and the floor you just walked across are designed. So is the air you are breathing and the passing clouds you just viewed. The birds you heard singing and the babies you heard cooing. The types of food you ate and the water you drank. The bed you slept on last night and the means to fall asleep.

I make use of the two major pathways that address our presence on this planet, that is the theory of evolution and Intelligent Design(ID). I show how they do or don't connect to an innate, long term plan. **The theory of evolution expects us to believe that billions of yet-undiscovered, connecting, converging steps will be found to explain our presence, while Intelligent Design expects us to make a leviathan leap of faith that we all came about by some intelligent entity, basically extraterrestrials or God.** In fact, when one really gets down to it, both are faith issues. Suppose for an instance that the theory of evolution were partially correct, then couldn't the huge (uncountable) number of steps with wide gaps between species be Intelligently Guided? Aren't they all designs, too? Just missing links? **Indeed, the God of the Gaps theory may be correct.**

I have wondered if re-creating man (if that's even possible) or a facsimile (a considerably easier model) might actually be one of our purposes in life. In addition to these above, there are many cherished reasons for being here including glorifying[1] God, country, and other people, cherishing parents, helping the poor, caring for the sick and the lame, living long and finding happiness.

Creating humanoids may be critical to our survival. Experts feel that we might be on our way to extinction. And, indeed, there are very real grounds to be concerned, from the micro- and macro-pollution in our oceans and the air we breathe to the potentials for

---

1 To glorify is often interpreted as to know, to love and to reveal His Essence.

nuclear accidents and wars. The planet will surely survive us in some fashion, but we may not survive us.

I have both a Bachelor's Degree in Biology (as a James Scholar) and Medical Degree from the University of Illinois, plus I have done two years research in Immunology as a research fellow. I have nine books published, six fiction and three non-fiction. *What Darwin Didn't Know* and *Billions of Missing Links* primarily address intelligent design (ID). I have been a Fellow with the Discovery Institute in Seattle. I have lectured across the United States as well as abroad in Israel and Spain, and spoken on local, national and international radio. My talks usually focus on evidence that supports an intelligence behind our being and the increasing problems believing the theory of evolution. I'm certain, Darwin gave it his best guess, based on the science of the mid-nineteenth century, but there's so much more now known. Every answer these days leads to many more questions. Somewhere along the line common sense must play in. It has been under-used.

Biological processes have always fascinated me. I was once a believer in the theory of evolution; I still agree with certain aspects such as natural selection. Surely, the fastest cheetah or the quietest rabbit has an advantage. I know all of the arguments (pro and con), perhaps better than many of Darwinian advocates. Most of my teachers, including those in graduate school, taught evolution as if it were already proven, the "tried and true" explanation for us being here. I was always one of the nodding heads. I've read Charles Darwin, Stephan Jay Gould, Daniel Dennett, Richard Dawkins, and many of the like. Much of what they had to say made sense to me, then. At times, it even seemed as if the theory of evolution's explanation were a "done deal." Dawkins' "Gene" seemed truly selfish.

Nonetheless, I never understood quite how it got to be so selfish. Some magic potion, I suppose. What was missing in all of the texts was that spark of life. The original ignition switch. Who or what flipped that critical switch. Plus, who's talking to whom in my mind. In your mind, too? Is there really a soul? Is that it? Did the soul show up at the moment of birth? At 32 weeks in utero, 25 weeks, 10 weeks or at conception? No one knows, of course.

My attitude toward the miracle of life began to change when I delivered my first baby. This little guy was a healthy, seven pounder. I was a fourth-year medical student who was trembling at the thought of standing between the legs of a woman I had never met and literally catching the most slippery pass ever thrown to me. I thought for sure I would drop him, but I didn't. Delivering a baby turned out to be an exhilarating experience. Sounds trite, I know, but it truly was exciting. And, this guy wasn't even my child.

I was never an atheist, more so an agnostic and sometimes a fox-hole-believer until later years, but hearing that first breath, and then the first cry, was riveting. How did this tiny thing know to breathe at that exact moment (without a slap)? Or suckle? Or poop? Later, the tiniest hand, that I had ever seen, grabbed hold of my pinkie. Here was a brand new person, as innocent as a living being can get, headed for a future with pre-loaded genetic blueprints—his unique roadmap for life. That was one of a hundred similar experiences I had in my training. Each birth seemed liked a miracle. All systems had properly converged and were maturing together per plan.

From that point on, I began to realize the human body was way too complex to simply settle for guesses, hunches, obsolete scientific studies, scholarly dogma and Just-So stories on how we got here. Much of Darwin's theories don't fit, now. Certainly not, when one gets down to that micro-world. Evolution of one species into another, rather than simply changing traits like fur color, was hard to believe. Yet, religious explanations for our being made it seem more like we were tropical fish dropped into a brand new aquarium. Envision whales drop from invisible hand in the sky. That, too, was hard to accept.

In my thirties, I stumbled on a book by Francis Hitching called *The Neck of the Giraffe*. It was an intriguing read. Since then, I've probably re-read it a dozen times. Years later, I still cite it as a great reference. The book challenged many of the common notions in the theory of evolution using a current scientific facts. Therein, I learned how the fossil record was seriously incomplete, meaning flawed and how changes from monkeys to humans didn't really work. Hitching pointed out that evolution cannot explain the extremely long neck of the giraffe, the blowhole on a whale, why the whale's tail moves up and down (not sideways like other sea creatures), why monkeys have more chromosomes than we (not less), and the double spray emitted from the backend of the bombardier beetle that explodes when the two chemicals combine. (Note they are entirely benign while chambered separately) If the predator (like a frog) is not deterred by the facial irritant (the explosion), it will readily spit the beetle out. You can easily find this on You tube.

Hitching pointed out that lateral parts of jaw bones of ancient creatures could not have changed from two bones into three, simultaneously moved up both sides of the head and evolved into inner ears of mammals, all by accident. That required pre-planning and foresight. Life processes are loaded with changes that anticipate future needs. I've always been curious why the fish, walking out of the sea, had the foresight to have lungs to breathe air (not water), appropriate legs to walk on hot sand and a digestive system ready to handle new kinds of food that fish have never seen. These are convergent designs. Is recreating ourselves (F)foresight? The evidence suggests it's a possibility.

Robots are loaded with converging designs, the electrical systems to the mechanical systems. They are looking more and more like us, soon-to-be humanoids. They talk and answer, even give advice using our voices. One even does backflips—I'm not sure why. Will we need humanoids to carry out our work after we destroy all living species on this plant? The answer is a not-too-soft yes. Unless black holes turn out to be short cuts to habitable planets, aliens give us a ride-along, or we learn to fly faster than light, only humanoids will be able to travel to the farthest reaches of outer space. Humans are too fragile, too needy.

I believe understanding past patterns will help predict future plans. Knowing if we are the result of accidents or consequences of Intelligent Design should also be very helpful.

"So God created man in his own image, in the image of God created He him; male and female created He them."

GENESIS 1:27, KING JAMES VERSION (KJV)

"We are survival machines - - robot vehicles blindly programmed to preserve the selfish molecules known as genes."

RICHARD DAWKINS, AUTHOR OF THE SELFISH GENE AND THE GOD DELUSION

"All the days ordered for me were written in Your Book before one of them came to be."

PSALM 139:16, NEW INTERNATIONAL VERSION OF THE BIBLE(NIV)

"If God were created, God wouldn't be God. God's Creator would be God. But the same people who ask 'Who created God?' would then ask 'Who created God's Dad?' "

DENNIS PRAGER, RADIO HOST AND AUTHOR OF THE RATIONAL BIBLE.

"Will robots inherit the Earth? Yes, but they will be our children."

MARVIN MINSKY, SCIENTIFIC AMERICAN, 1994.

I
What Is A Human Being?

The keys on a keyboard have the capability of writing all novels, poems, encyclopedias, government policies, computer programs and scientific papers, but it takes an intelligence to press the keys in the right order, at the right time. If the lettered keys were genes of a single human being, it would take at least 30,000 keys(genes), and maybe as many as 100,000 keys (genes)[2], to complete a human blueprint. But, note many(maybe most) genes combine and recombine, work in groups of two, three and even dozens, and jump around in unbelievable, and seemingly directed ways. The actual number of genetic possibilities is way beyond measuring. Maybe, way beyond calculating.

Before proceeding to create a human being, one needs to define what a human being is, which is not an easy task. There are many definitions to be had. The question brings to mind the old story of a group of five blind men coming upon an adult male elephant and attempting to describe it. This was an animal that none of them had ever encountered before. The parable comes from India and it's an ancient story about people claiming to know absolute truth,

---

2 The number of genes in humans have varied from 100K down to 20K and back to 30K. The total number, due to overlapping controls and function such as epigenetic and RNA contributions, has not been determined.

yet having limited knowledge. Even though each one's experience might be true and accurate, it may not be the entire truth.

One blind man feels the tail and says that an elephant is like a rope, another feels the body and says it has to be a wall, another feels the massive leg and insists it must be a pillar, another feels the trunk and says it's a snake with thick skin, and the last feels the tusk and emphatically states it must be something like a weapon, maybe a spear. All become angry out of frustration with the stupidity of the others and soon come to blows. This is resolved when a sighted man intervenes and fully describes an elephant. They realize they could have painted a much more accurate picture if they had only combined their knowledge.

Past and some present-day scientific studies are like each blind man's impression. One must always have the total picture. And, we don't. **We should not be temporal chauvinists confined by the bars of time**.

I also sometimes wonder if our scientific and political community isn't like the characters portrayed in the H.G.Wells 1904 short story: "The Country of the Blind." Therein all of the inhabitants of a remote valley have been blind for generations yet do remarkably well. When a sighted man accidentally falls from a mountain top into their valley, and later falls in love with one of the women, the elders insist his descriptions of an outside world are heretic and delusional. They demand that his eyes be poked out.

Miriam Webster Dictionary simply defines a human being as a bipedal primate mammal (Homo sapiens). For me, this falls way short. Lots of animals are primates and bipedal. Given that definition, an alien from outer space might confuse us with apes or maybe kangaroos. A person seated in a wheelchair or lying flat in bed might be considered a different species. An amputee might be inexplicable.

Wikipedia states in that humans have manual dexterity and heavy tool use as compared to other animals; open-ended and complex language compared to other animal communications; and a general trend toward larger, more complex brains and societies. It fails to say a word about what we look like or how we act. What we actually think about. That is, if we even think.

According to Goodman, humans (taxonomically Homo sapiens) are the only extant members of the subtribe Hominina. They are characterized by erect posture and bipedal locomotion; high manual dexterity and heavy tool use compared to other animals; open-ended and complex language use compared to other animal communications; and a general trend toward larger, more complex brains and societies[3]. Definitely closer, but do we lay eggs or procreate in numerous ways?

Wikipedia quoting K. Burke[4], in his classic text, says: "man is distinct from other creatures by virtue of his use of symbols to communicate, his understanding of negation, his separation from nature by his own techniques, his existence in differing social structures, and his goal to become better than he presently is." Try this definition out on the residents of the tenderloin district of San Francisco.

Ask a biochemist and he or she might answer we are 65% oxygen, 18.5% carbon dioxide, 9.5 hydrogen, 3.2% nitrogen. 1.5% calcium, 1.0% phosphorus and about a dozen more minerals make up another 1.0%. Another biology authority might say we're mostly water with fats, proteins, bone products, carbohydrates and sugar, DNA, and RNA and not worth a dime if split into components. A tissue expert might say we're connective tissue, bones, muscle, and nerve tissue, at least 200 different types of cells and an uncountable number of bacteria, inside and out. If an alien were given this information, it might think we reside in a bucket.

---

3 Goodman M, Tagle D, Fitch D, Bailey W, Czelusniak J, Koop B, Benson P, Slightom J (19.90) "Primate Evolution at the DNA Level and a Classification of Hominoids". *J Mol Evol.* **30** (3): 260–66. Bibcode:1990JMolE..30..260G. doi:10.1007/BF02099995. PMID 2109087

4 Burke, K., *Language as Symbolic Action* Berkeley & Los Angeles. University of California Press, 1966) 16.

An electrophysiologist might define humans as a walking collection of electrical circuits. We know there are electrical fields surrounding our bodies, our heart beats are carried out by electrical pulses, all actions of the brain are preceded by electrical impulses, thoughts an electrical hurricane; nerve signals with electrical information are sent throughout our bodies at lightning speeds. If one were to apply an electrical stimulus to the leg muscle of a frog, it would retract, or to the arm muscle of a monkey, its hand would make a fist.

We are primarily made of saline (salt and water) which is a great conductor of electricity and generally life-sustaining. Could this be an accident? Was this because we once came from the sea or that simply saline is a good thing for living beings? A neurosurgeon can stimulate a section of human brain and cause a long forgotten image(s) to come to mind in his patient. There are trillions(+) of electrical impulses traveling back and forth, in and out, up and down, and inside individual cells throughout our body, making us much more complicated than Verizon, Sprint, Xfinity and AT&T, combined. A smart phone, given the right technology, could be powered by our brain.

A carney at a circus might define many of us as fools. A waitress thinks we are good or bad tippers and slow or fast eaters. A warden may consider his prisoners as crooks in-training to become better crooks. Might politicians think of us as gullible sheep? Aren't women considered only baby makers and men only sperm donors by some? The clergy considers us a member of the flock. Lost souls who need guidance?

Bed bugs probably would view humans as a Godsend shedder of skin cells. Billions of dead and dying cells fly off of us all day long as we walk, talk and sleep. The stronger the wind, the greater the flurry. The air in a nudist colony must have a constant, yet invisible, blizzard of dead cells. How fun? A mosquito must consider humans as a bearer of life-sustaining blood. As might a tick. A mountain lion would consider us breakfast, lunch and dinner. So might a flea.

The Bible says we were created in the image of God, but there are very few images, if any, to know what that means. Many say it's spiritual only. God spoke to Moses through a burning bush. I think it's safe to say our image is not burning bushes. When Moses asked God to show him his glory, the Bible quotes God as saying: "You cannot see my face, for man shall not see me and live" and "Behold there is a place by me where you can stand on the rock, and while my glory passes by I will put you in a cleft of the rock, and I will cover you with my hand until I have passed by. Then I will take away my hand, and you shall see my back, but my face shall not be seen.[5]" What God's hand and back look like remains unknown.

God gave us a body and soul. "Then, the Lord God formed man of dust from the ground and breathed into his nostrils the breath of life, and man became a living soul.[6]" Defining the body is a lot easier than the soul. I will attempt to do both. The soul, in particular, is critical as we are well on the way to sharing our place here with or being replaced by artificial intelligence(AI); some experts predict AI will surpass us by 2046. That moment is called Singularity.

Was Sex Designed To Be Fun?

On the surface, that may seem like a silly question. Of course it is, but sex has to be fun. Not an uncomfortable requirement. Would we have had kids if sex were pure drudgery? It goes without saying that the wanting to have (and having) intercourse with the opposite sex is critical to the re-creation and survival of our family, our species, our gene pool. At least, that's how it's been for a long time.

In the future, some of us might remain celibate and simply purchase, adopt or rent humanoid children. This, I think, will happen. Robots, like pets, might be adequate company for some of us.

5 Exodus 33: 20-23 *King James Version*
6 Genesis 2:7 *King James Version*

In contrast to pets, one doesn't need a plastic bag along when taking a robotic child for a walk. There's something bothersome, however, about owning a seven year-old that never changes and repeats first grade every year. Maybe, one can trade it in for a second grader? And, so on?

Cloning will likely become a doable option, especially as sperm counts continue to dwindle worldwide. Fortunately, we're not in jeopardy (yet?), but counts have dropped 50% in some Western nations. This approach lends itself quite well to the narcissists among us. If the world only had more of me, what a wonderful place it might be. What if I had enough money to make a hundred of me? Or a thousand of me? I'm sure, there will be wealthy people who will think that way. If another Einstein comes along or Beethoven, might it behoove us to clone this person before he/she dies?

Growing functional male and female parts in the laboratory may sound like science fiction, but it is not that far off. We already grow bladders, white cells, skin, bone, heart muscle, prostate cells and parts of a human brain in the lab. In fact, human brain cells growing in culture will actually send out tendrils to make a connection. Might we eventually grow complete living beings? Could be. Starfish can grow a new starfish from the tiniest pieces of their body. So can certain worms. If it's true that every cell in the body carries all the blueprints, it's just a matter of tapping into the right DNAs.

We are also getting close to artificial gestation, that is from conception to "birth". In the past fifty years we have gone from saving babies 36 weeks old to tiny premies at 23 weeks old with special incubators, IVs and lighting. Earlier periods of gestation are being conducted with lambs. Imagine a time when women will be freed up from the toils and dangers of pregnancy. Just pick out the sperm with the DNA characteristics you like (or ask for donation), harvest a "ripe" egg from a favorable surrogate, pay up front as you leave (VISA is fine) and watch your child grow inside a plastic bag for nine months. DNA editing can easily be done.

Which species started the reproductive process with intercourse is unclear. There doesn't seem to be any trial and error samples among the fossils. Seems as if all species got it right the first time through. But, who can tell? Evolution theory would have us believe that we eased into our present method of reproduction around dinosaur days or 210 million years ago (MYA) when rodent-sized mammals were running about. Until we find a fossil with a male and female actually copulating, proof will have to wait.

The process of reproduction was and is much easier when bacteria and algae divide in half. And, then half again. That's called asexual reproduction and, even that didn't come about easily. It required billions of steps, all happening in the right ways. Asexual sex obviously didn't work as well in animals as large as dinosaurs. We think that female fish have always laid eggs and then the males deposited their sperm there about, i.e. external fertilization. Lizards, a species that is considered to be further down the line in evolution, kept their eggs internal and engaged in intercourse. Amphibians, the presumed in-between species, tended to do reproduction like fish. There is some logic in this progression, but it's not possible.

Way too many beneficial mutations would have been needed to explain internal fertilization. Possibly trillions. Natural selection doesn't come close to explaining it. One could argue, there was once a survival benefit to shifting to internal fertilization? No need to protect the nest as the baby-holder went wherever mom went. With longer, more complex gestation, the offspring had to reside inside. **There zero evidence that there was a reproductive process (single step) in-between external and internal fertilization.**

With rare exception such as bonobos, we are the only species who commonly engage in intercourse during the off-season, meaning when the female is not in heat. In fact, humans usually cannot tell when ovulation has occurred. Men cannot, for sure. We are mostly driven by 24/7 built-in desires, visual cues, hormones, another's seductive behavior, chemical scents (pheromones) opportunities and texts. When we fall in love, we're happier because love is a wonderful thing and/or in love feels good because dopamine is released, more possessive because of vasopressin increases, obsessive because of elevated adrenaline and norepinephrine, sweaty with heart racing because of adrenaline (and aroused), a glow in our face from the autonomic system (also pupils dilate), and oddly, is more tolerant of pain[7] because we are distracted. Might we be programmed to get excited about opportunities to reproduce?

It's not just falling in love that can lead to intercourse, however. It can be falling in lust, which is a close, overlapping facsimile. One might say our nose knows as there is a tiny, specialized section in each nasal passage that receives chemical signals that others secrete in their sweat. Our axillary hair and pubic hair act as wicks. Oddly, those are the same areas we wash the most vigorously; biology would suggest we might do the opposite. Go figure.

Lust usually lasts for a short time, such as a one-nighter, but it can linger a lifetime. But, does it matter if babies are produced, which may be one of our main purposes in life. **Programmed deaths requires programmed births.**

Can that deeper feeling called love stem from something outside our genes?

Most of us have an eagerness to see the opposite sex in a variety of seductive situations. The enticing scents of perfumes and colognes and types of clothing (or the lack of clothing), spur us on. No other species purposefully teases the opposite sex by hiding their genitals (or breasts) for reasons of seduction. Other species tend to display them (everything that is relevant) and visually emphasize select items when it's time.

What makes sex enjoyable (and doable), in part, is simultaneous development of complimentary sexual organs. That means human testes, prostate, penis are perfectly matched with human ovaries, uterus and vagina. An initial mismatch anywhere along evolution

---

7 "What Happens When I Fall in Love?" *Science Focus*, p83 (February 2019).

might have prevented the arrival of many species including us. Could it be luck that it always happened correctly. The odds are astronomical. Two human partners must come under the spell of each other's pheromones. Dousing pig pheromones won't help humans procreate and pouring human pheromones on pigs will likely add nothing. Pheromones that are malodorous or irritating to the eye just won't cut it, either. Compatible or reciprocal pheromones had to have evolved at the same time. How this may happen with a newly acquainted partner is unclear.

A man needs the right biological machinery to make sperm by the millions—small numbers won't work-oftentimes in quick succession, plus he must keep them somewhat cool(in external sacs) than the inside of his body plus place them in a fluid for easy transport, and ejaculate them in a forceful way, in appropriate place and at the correct moment. Too early and too late are detrimental. None of this could have come about by accident. There are many exacting steps and considerable foresight.

A woman needs a way to create and store 500,000 immature ova(eggs) or approximately quarter of million inside each ovary. Under most circumstances, her body only selects one per month or about 360 over a lifetime. No one knows how a specific egg is chosen among so many options. There is some thought that the extruded egg is somehow selected to match up with the male partner's genetics. Perhaps, it's his looks, beard, way of thinking, pheromones or some yet to be described aura. It's the eternally optimistic ovaries.

Note the sexual organs have to be in strategic locations on the body to work together. There is no proof that through trial and error, natural selection or mutation these locations came about.

Before fertilization, the egg disengages (literally pops out) and drops directly into the waiting, sticky, fingerlike ends of the fallopian tube, where it is caught like a baseball. Locations were pre-planned. Tiny projections transport it (roll it) down a funnellike tube toward the uterus. I once compared this long, exacting trip to golf ball traveling from a golf course to another course far away and making a hole in one. If it is not fertilized within a very specific timeframe, it will continue through the uterus and be eliminated along with the sloughed wall of the uterus. This, too, is, another completed process that needs specific programming and foresight. Failure afterwards to clear everything attached to the uterine wall can result in infection, even death. Menstrual periods have very specific programs and timing.

There are many requirements, not the least of which the sperm have to be sturdy enough to swim the equivalent of many miles at greater than (relatively speaking) Olympic speeds. They must travel in groups of millions as the trip inward is treacherous and challenging. They must overcome obstacles, sometimes using a buddy or team system, sometimes fighting off competitors (so called sperm wars) to fertilize an egg which may only want a specific sperm and not all of you guys.

The evolution of man would have failed if their sperm were weak swimmers or didn't know where they were going (and what to do when they got there). The ultimate winner may not be the first to arrive. There might be some spelled-out parameters that open the gate. Maybe mom's body had decided it wants genes for a redhead this time—we don't know if true. Once the winner gets inside, the egg seals off all entryways and continues its trek to the womb where it will implant and grow in very specific, orderly ways.

Some say the act of kissing is simply the sharing of pheromones. We lap this up when we're young, simply by making-out for hours. Later on, we adults tend to "cut to the chase" much sooner. Try to imagine a two-hour, X-rated movie with 105 minutes of only making out. Wouldn't earn much at the box office.

Having sex must have been made to be as irresistible as possible from the outset. Why bother otherwise? Food, water and shelter have always been demanding.

During those reproductive years, it helps to wear one's most attractive birthday suit. Be the cutest, the prettiest, the most buff, the most handsome, and/or the most personable. These days it might be the loudest stereo, the strongest perfume or the wildest tattoo(s). In many instances that also means looking and acting young. Nature has made certain we look and act our best when we are most likely to attract partners and procreate. The different parts also work their best when one is young. Sperm dwindle and change with age, breasts fall and vaginas dry. Intercourse many times per day belong to the young mostly as it adds to the chances of catching the egg at the right moment. Pheromone-induced excitement wanes with time in many relationships. Perhaps, one "tires" of or gets used to the other person's pheromones. That's where love and caring, shared interest and goals, and cherished experiences step in. All programmed?

The Chicken Or Egg Conundrum.

An interesting question, and a new twist, to ask an atheist might be: what came first, a woman or an ovum. And, how might that have happened. Both must have arrived simultaneously, as did every aspect of a woman's body. And, indeed, as did every aspect of a man's body. There's no need to do an experiment to prove this happened. Sometimes only common sense is needed. This is akin to Dr. Marcos Eberlin's[8] answer to the old chicken and egg question: "The chicken-and-egg problem is the archetypical example of casual circularity. To get A we need B, but to get B we first need A. We cannot have one without the other. To get both together, we need foresight—an engineer capable of planning for the future."

A brand new human being begins at conception, when the egg is fertilized by the uber-capable, ultra-smart, most athletic sperm that

---

8 A Professor from Brazil , Director of the Discovery-Mackenzie Research Center for Science, Faith and Society, member of the Brazilian Academy of Sciences, and author of *Foresight: How the Chemistry of Life Reveals Planning and Purpose*. He has 1000 scientific papers published. Recorded in The Stream https://stream.org/chicken-and-egg-problem-biology/

matches up with the egg's requirements. Billions upon billions of divisions follow over nine months — all converging plans or designs; later, the egg evolves into a 30-40 trillion-cell human being with amazing precision and speed. That includes over 100,000 divisions per second (on average during the later stages) with a greater than 99.999% rate of accuracy, following very specific blueprints.

By the 16th day the fetus's heart starts beating. By the thirtieth day, the embryo has grown 10,000X. At seven weeks the baby is an inch long and has developed all organs (e.g. liver, sex organs, spleen, intestine). At eight weeks fingerprints and toe-prints show up and the beginnings of a brain can be seen. At a specific moment, 250,000 neurons (nerve cells) migrate (climb, crawl, slide) every minute to designated places with distinct purpose(s) within the brain. At twelve weeks vocal cords show up, but because the lung is filled with amniotic fluid, the baby remains silent and does not take a breath. Crying, too, while enveloped in amniotic fluid would be fatal. **This had to be Foresight.**

Ultrasound studies have shown unborn babies at four months sucking their thumbs and playing with their umbilical cord. Between 18 and 20 weeks the senses for pain are mature, virtually the same as they will be at birth. Studies show babies withdrawing their feet to eternal stimuli[9]. Some premature babies at 21-22 weeks can survive in a neonatal intensive care unit. At twenty-eight weeks, a baby will track a moving light such as a flashlight up against mom's belly. At twenty-four weeks, an ultrasound can show the baby smiling. All along the baby is getting bigger and different organ systems are maturing. The last three months, in particular, have more to do with enlarging and maturing and much less with developing new systems. At the time of birth, the mother's body has decided the

---

9 Charlotte Lozier Institute, "The Science of Fetal Pain at 20 Weeks," https://s27589. pcdn.co/wp-content/uploads/2018/12/Science-of-Fetal-Pain-Fall-2018.pdf

child is ready. It's a little like fruit. Greenish bananas are ok, but fully yellow ares best

An overarching architectural plan is in place from the very start. This information, with a few exceptions, seems to exist inside the nucleus of every cell; certain chapters are chosen based on specific, timely needs. For example, if it's the development of heart tissue, the chapters might break down into pacemakers, chambers, coronary circulation and valves. Each of these can be broken down into more detailed chapters and indeed, those breakdowns can go even further.

At forty weeks, the baby is ready for delivery. This becomes the most dangerous event of any individual's life. That is, short of one's deathbed, of course. Passage through the birth canal must be precisely coordinated. The taking of the first breath must be exact. Off by more than a few seconds can mean permanent brain damage, even death. An artery that bypasses the lungs, while in utero, must promptly close or death ensues. That means oxygen no longer comes from the placenta, which is about to slough.

As the fetus grows it needs blood cells, but before that it needs a heart to pump, pipelines to travel through. It will need lung cells to absorb oxygen, but before that it will need an airway system and pipelines with blood cells to carry oxygen away. Because there has to be a way to eliminate metabolic products there must be kidneys, ureters and a bladder plus external changes, These are just a few of chicken and egg conundrums. If a baby is born before the moment it should take that first breath, it dies. Too late, it dies. The newborn must be able to roll over before crawling, lift its head and chest before it can sit up; it needs normal functioning vocal cords (in the right place) to cry, to tell the world that it has needs. All foresight?

The point is that complexity upon complexity supports design with purpose theory. Evolution can explain some lesser, intra-species changes like stronger members of a species reproducing stronger offspring. Maybe there were some accidents and coincidences along the way resulting in a few unexplained changes. Maybe.

An Exercise In Converging Designs

Enormous and complex changes occur and re-occur as the cells change and mature throughout the nine months of gestation. The fertilized egg immediately divides in half and then those cells divide in half, and then they divide, so on and so on, many, many billions of times, often changing appearances and roles. The mechanisms to make new chemicals, proteins and hormones constantly appear. New functions and new jobs show up. Somehow, these cells know how to change, where to go, how to get there, how to set up shop, what roles to assume and how to interact with neighbors and distant cells. Virtually every, normal human heart looks the same and works the same. Skin on the nose closely resembles skin on the cheeks, yet slightly adapted. The left eyeball closely resembles the right eyeball, but reversed. The right arm grows at the same rate as the left arm; and the legs match. Our right and left halves are mirror images.

The fertilized egg has all of a person's blueprints. A built-in internet of instructions. The next cells know which blueprints to draw from, and those, in turn, may use some other portions. And so, it happens down the line.

During some of my lectures I sometimes use the example of an ultra-huge, collapsing domino puzzle to demonstrate the changes a fetus makes in the womb. There's a succession of modifying steps with trillions of in-between steps, all happening at similar times or in succession, throughout the body, and in the right order. It would take a lifetime for someone to draw the diagrams as we know them. And, I would guess, by the time he/she has finished, the newest revisions might take another lifetime. As we learn more, we understand less.

To begin, first envision a domino puzzle large enough to fill Central Park. From high above, it closely resembles a human baby in three-dimension. You can pick the sex. I don't care. Different-colored, vertically standing dominos represent different organs such as the liver, kidneys, brain, adrenal glands, intestines, bones, sex organs and the heart. Red is arteriole blood and blue is venous blood. White is bone and gray/white is brain. Pretend when a domino falls, it means that part(cell) has been created by the previous domino.

You have a reserved seat midway up the baby, about even with its navel. Bring binoculars and a snack.

This puzzle has twenty-five trillion, standard-sized, vertically standing dominos with an additional, quadrillion(+) smaller dominos veering off in smaller, spirals, pipelines and circles forming a myriad of different human-specific shapes. An additional quintillion(+) microscopic dominos, that are hard to see, veer off to form microscopic cells. I purposefully skipped the even smaller dominos that form the innards of every cell.

It took a team of millions many years to set this up (as you might guess), working 24/7. To lessen errors, tiny correcting RNA machines travel back and forth along the different lines of dominos. Other vehicles bring nourishment and fluids.

The fertilized egg, or starter domino, is located near the middle of the puzzle, deep within the pelvis. It is slightly larger than all of the other dominos and has a pearly sheen. It can be tipped over by remote control. This is your job. At the right moment, you will be asked to press a button to cause fertilization.

The timer strikes zero and you start the process. The first domino tips forward, striking two dominos in front of it, and they tip forward striking four, and so on. A loudening clickety-clack, series of chain reactions follow as dozens, then hundreds, then thousands, simultaneously collapse, They go off in every three dimensional direction. They form a host of spectacular colorful designs of a baby. Within these designs, smaller designs by smaller dominos happen. Some lines of dominos seem to climb stairs, others set go down stairs, some set off sparks, others start marbles winding down tracts to knock over other dominos, set off flickering lights, and create a variety of sounds. The crashing sounds are almost deafening. Any faltering or misplaced dominos are quickly fixed by tiny correction vehicles. If any one domino fails to fall, or falls incorrectly, all of the dominos beyond that point do not fall and the "organ" never forms. This is what one might call a mutation and the higher up the chain, the worse consequences. A death knell.

Red dominos, located near the center, start painting a picture of a four-chambered heart with valves and gray ones an electrical pathway for stimulation. At the same time, two, lighter red parallel lines leave the heart and start producing several tubelike structures(arteries) that wind around, split and split again, diminishing in size as they reach distant areas (representing capillaries). Each tube contains smaller collapsing puzzles of tiny, light-red and white dominos, representing red and white blood cells. Blue dominos soon clickety-clack back, forming blue tubelike structures (veins) of increasing size. Within are bluish red blood cells.

At the same time, pink-grayish dominos fall into the shape of two lungs situated along each side the heart. Mahogany dominos form the liver and spleen, located just below a thin, tan diaphragm. Greenish dominos paint both kidneys, with lines(tubes) going downward into a centrally located, dark pale pink bladder full of yellowish dominos. White dominos, for bones, form the skull, the back bones, the hips and all extremity bones. Pink muscles line the bones and attach at select points. Different shades of pink and tan form the esophagus, stomach, small bowel and large bowel. Skin is a nondescript, thin, light tan line of dominos, outlining every aspect of the baby. Many of these processes occur together.

At the opposite end, smaller dominos simultaneously start forming the brain. The exterior layer is a dull white, while the interior is light gray. There are numerous red and blue tubes (blood vessels) weaving in and out. Size is deceptive as nearly half of the total dominos making up a human baby, reside within the brain.

One might represent the growth and formation of all living entities in similar ways, just add or subtract select numbers of colors of dominos, emphasize some and de-emphasize some, from the smallest submicroscopic species to the largest animals. Every step, everywhere, every time, is dependent on the preceding step(s). Many of these steps cannot do a thing if not connected up. A misplaced or damaged domino (a mutation) stops the progression of everything downstream. No new information (a new puzzle or piece) spontaneously happens on its own, once started, unless corrections are part of the blueprints. And, this actually happens.

It might be interesting to revisit a famous quote, and its meaning, from Darwin at this juncture. **It is a major flaw in Darwin's theory.** Note: **"If it could be demonstrated that any complex organ existed, which could not possibly have been formed by numerous, slight modifications, my theory would absolutely break down. But I can find no such case."**

Darwin's "successive slight modifications" is the equivalent of "numerous" dominos falling over (or steps) to form a heart or a brain(an "organ"), whereas it actually takes trillions, all of which have complicated, timed interactions. More simply, is a wooden bridge functional after each individual plank is set? Not at all. It's useless until all the planks are in place as well as the foundation and guard rails. There are virtually no incomplete bridges in Nature.

Or, he meant the change from one species to another, such as apes to humans. His writings could mean either. Yet, Darwin had no knowledge of genetics, embryology, or physiology. He had no idea how the heart or brain really worked. No idea that thyroid hormone existed. Or, antibodies. Or, hemoglobin. In fact, he didn't know a cell existed—that came years after his death. He had no idea why a child resembles his parent. He had no clue what controlled growth, what stopped bleeding, how infections were fought and what initiated the feeling of hunger. His idea of evolution was no more than getting your car painted a new color or changing the upholstery.

Do We All March To The Same Drum?

The blueprints for every human being, whether a person is tall, short, skinny, obese, black, brown, white, red or yellow, are all extremely similar. In fact, 99.99% similar. We might look a little different with blond or black hair, blue or brown eyes and a small or large nose, but that's mostly trim. With rare exceptions we all have two eyes, one nose and one mouth in the same positions, bum in the back, and scalp at the top.

Barring the consequences of illnesses and injuries, we all have very similar internal operations working to keep all of our trains running on time. There are mechanisms to keep the heart beating at appropriate rates, the brain thinking, controlling and reacting, the kidneys cleaning the blood, the bone marrow manufacturing blood cells, the lymph nodes making antibodies, and the gut squeezing foodstuffs along. To name just a few. We all need water, essentially in the same amounts. We all need rest, in virtually the same amounts. We assume, with good reason, but no proof, we each see the colors of the rainbow exactly the same way, hear trombones and flutes the same and taste bananas. The exceptions might be found in children who don't like the taste of something, but other agendas may be in play. Also, non-beer drinkers claim they cannot stand the taste of beer. I know from giving lectures, we all don't like the same jokes.

The design of the human body seems to follow some very specific mathematic rules. Some of these configurations are called Divine proportions, the Golden Number (1.614), the Golden Ratio, Golden Rectangle and Golden Spiral. They come from the Islamic Golden Age. Artists have known this intuitively for centuries. Famous painters make use of these proportions, including Seurat, Botticelli, Raphael and Michelangelo. These ratios are also found in famous architecture such Taj Mahal, the Pyramids, Parthenon, and Notre Dame. Even the Lady Blunt Stradivarius[10].

Davinci's Vitruvian Man, the muscular and symmetric male standing inside a square inside a circle, is a classic example of design: indeed, it can be found on the cover of my book *What Darwin Didn't Know* and discussed therein. Note a seven-foot tall basketball player would have a near seven foot arm span. Pediatricians commonly predict a child's ultimate height by doubling their height at age two years. There are clearcut patterns that are followed.

Other signs suggesting the use of mathematics are ratio of the forearm to the upper arm which has a measurable, positive impact on lifting, and the ratio of the upper leg to the lower leg has a major impact on walking. Where the ligaments and tendons lay are critical to all actions. In ancient days physicians measured humans in heads, fists and cubits. In general, a human is seven and half heads tall. The forearm ratio to the hand is almost always 1.614. Ancient artists drew the ideal person at eight heads and the heroic individual at eight and half heads. The distance between both eyes are purposefully one eye length apart. A lot of math and enormous signs of design can be found within the eye. The ears and even the nasal passages are mathematically separated for best function. Artists often point out the numerous triangles, often with two or three equal sides. There's one from the outer edge of the eyes to the tip of the nose and another from the tip of the nose to the sides of the lips. There's a triangle from the shoulders to navel, another from the navel to the hips and one from the pubis to the shoulders.

Many, if not all, Laws of Nature can be described in mathematical terms. Stand outs when it comes to biological design are the

---

10 Gary B. Meisner, *The Golden Ratio: The Divine Beauty of Mathematics* (Race Point , 2018.)

Fibonacci Numbers and the Golden Ratio. Much of our body proportions fit these rules.

Leonardo Fibonacci was an Italian mathematician from the Republic of Pisa who lived c1175-c1250. He is the author of Liber Abaci which popularized the Hindu-Arabic numeral system. He is also regarded as the foremost mathematician of the Middle Ages. His discovery of sequence of numbers, which bear his name: 1, 1, 2, 3, 5, 8, 13, 21, 34, 55, 89, 144, 233, 377, represent many of the shapes (laws) found in the living world. This works if one adds one number with the next (start on the left with zero), the next is the answer.

One can find Fibonacci numbers if one counts the spiral scales of a pine cone, the petals of a flower (often 5), the spirals of Romanesque broccoli, the spiral of the spiral aloe, and the spiral of the sunflower. There's also an inherent ratio within these numbers of 1.618 called Phi which can be used to study the proportions of natural spirals as seen with the panther chameleon's tail, the monarch butterfly caterpillar, cochlea of the human ear, snail shells, the seahorse tail, the nautilus, many snail shells, spiral of one's fingerprint, the spiral of the Milky Way. All of these seem to follow natural laws.

Virtually all mammals, reptiles, amphibians and fish are symmetric. Short of an accident, no animal, to date, has an odd number of legs or arms. I would guess that the millipede have an even number of legs too, but haven't taken the time to count them. Wings are symmetric and so are select fins. What needs to be up front is up front; what needs to be in the back is in the back; what needs to depart the body, like digested food, leaves posterior and inferior, partially utilizing gravity.

The human blueprint (DNA) can also be discussed in mathematical terms and comes with organized plans for using every tool, every contrivance, every connection, every process/procedure, every lock and key, every twisted protein molecule, every reaction, every twist in every DNA and RNA molecule, every delivery vehicle, and all electrical charges. It's much like the measurements that engineers make before building any structure. For example, there could never be a bridge across Columbia River without very intense studies and planning. Or, the International Space Station. Yet, these are toys by comparison to human design.

Trillions of our parts fit precisely together like a huge, dynamic, 3-dimensional jigsaw puzzle. Nothing is wasted. None of it is junk or vestigial. What we don't understand should never be labeled useless. Proteins often look like interminably twisted skeins of yarn, yet there's a definite rhyme to the seeming madness in every twist, turn and fold. They fit into convoluted ports in very precise, reciprocal or complimentary parts.

". . . there are no demonstrated examples of unguided, mindless processes anticipating and solving problems that require a sophisticated orchestration of fine-tuned parts, all brought together for an origin event."

MARCOS EBERLIN[11]

11 Director of the Discovery-Mackenzie Research Center for Science, Faith and Society, member of the Brazilian Academy of Sciences, and author of *Foresight: How the Chemistry of Life Reveals Planning and Purpose*

II

Are We Here By Coincidence, Accident Or Design?

A coincidence means the appearance of a meaningful connection, yet none can be found. We tend to think of these as being nice events, even rewarding and wonderful, like winning a lottery when one rarely purchases a ticket. Or, running into an old friend just when you had been thinking of him or her. But, a coincidence can also be unpleasant. Or, worse. For example, walking out of a theater just as a gang fight erupts. Or, the murder of Rebecca Schaeffer, July 18, 1989. A crazed stalker with a loaded gun pushed the downstairs doorbell just when she was expecting a script for Godfather 3 and her intercom to check was not functioning. Most of us call this bad timing or bad luck, in the extreme, but they also fall into the category of bad coincidences.

An accident, on the other hand, is the occurrence of an unforeseen event; it's something that happens by chance even though it may have followed natural laws such as an apple falling on your head. Accidents are unintended like motor collisions or dropping something heavy on your big toe. They are unplanned. They can be painful. They can even be fatal.

The theory of evolution mostly fits the accidental definition, but there are a few interesting overlaps. Life supposedly began with an accidental lightning strike to an accidentally formed primordial soup that accidentally had the right combination of amino acids (protein precursors). Somehow the spark also had a way of kick starting life. Everything thereafter presumably followed the rules of Universal Laws of Nature, plus a sprinkling of mutations, which are typically damaging. Evolution is often called naturalism (meaning by Nature) or materialism and it excludes all spiritual and supernatural explanations. God is out.

The third term is Intelligent Design (ID), which can, to my way of thinking be divided into Intelligent Purpose and Intelligent Guidance. It simply means there is highly suggestive evidence that an intelligence was behind our origin. ID gave life a purpose (s) and helped mold the process(es), including some changes attributed to evolution.

As one delves into the DNA messaging of each cell, it becomes apparent that there's a complex information system running each of our lives. It had to be written by an incredible programmer. That could mean God did it, but it doesn't exclude some other intelligence such as aliens. A way to think of it is that you are enjoying a play, yet assuming all of the dialogue and background happened by accident. If Intelligent Design were to be argued in court as our creative agent, it might be labeled circumstantial evidence, basically meaning there were no witnesses. Certainly, none living today.

There is no forensic evidence, as we know it. No fingerprints, infra-red images or forensic DNA, either. Proof that macroevolution, as noted in Darwin's writings, does not even rise to the level of circumstantial evidence.

Billions of people across the globe believe that a certain God was our Designer. Yet, there are many millions who feel evolution makes sense and there's no God. These latter numbers have been increasing for decades. Both sides are deeply entrenched; both prospects are equally tough to prove. One might ask if they are mutually exclusive and I would posit maybe not. Mutations are usually negative, and damaging, but not always. Might some be positive and by Design? Natural selection works within species such as weeding out the elderly and the ill; the fastest are more likely to survive. Couldn't that be by Design?

The classic example given to argue design is the finding of a pocket watch on a trail in the woods and knowing that it couldn't have created itself. It's not the consequence of a watch seedling, a TIMEX mushroom or a quirky bunch of root springs that found each other by serendipity. And, so it goes with the human being. A watch shows design and purpose, but we, who are a trillion-fold more complicated, are thought to be an accident with a bunch of lucky breaks.

Aspects of microevolution, however are supported by facts and observation. That means the changes we see within species such as improving camouflage, different shaped beaks for different food sources, and/or more offspring when predators are abundant. We can breed horses to run faster or pull heavier loads and dogs to cuddle and or protect us. We can make many species smaller or larger, faster or slower, prettier or uglier. Look at the different colors of flowers that have been cultivated. That is, without changing the species.

We know microevolution changes happen within a species; this has resulted in over 400 species of horse. Although the American Kennel Club recognizes 192 breeds of dogs, experts feel there may be at least 340 breeds. This, however, is not the changing of one species into another. A cat can never become a rat. Or, vice versa. A fruit fly bombarded with radiation didn't change into a house fly, but, instead, grew extra legs attached to its head.

Was The Table Set For Us?

To assess the impact of coincidence, accident and/or (D)design on our beginnings, take a look at our position in the Milky Way. It seems unique; some say it's ideal. Author Arthur C. Clarke[12] has said, "Sometimes I think we are alone in the universe and sometimes I think we are not. In either case, the thought is quite staggering."

So far, astronomers have found over 5000 exoplanets, meaning planets outside our solar system, and none have shown any signs of life. But, maybe it's too early to be sure. SETI scientists have been seeking contact with extraterrestrials by radio since the early 1900s. No one has picked up the phone, yet. Could we be alone in the Universe; might all life here merely be a shape-shifting, mildew-like contagion that spoils an occasional planet, now and then? We do seem to be spoiling it.

The Milky Way is a swirling, spiral galaxy with two huge arms that contain over 400 billion stars. It is 100,000 light years across and 1000 light years thick. Even if we had the ability to reach distant stars, there's not enough time for a million, manned-ships to check out each planet and their moons. Our sun takes 225 million years to revolve around the center of the Milky Way, traveling at a speed over 500,000 mph. Note that motion, plus our own planet's spin of approximately 1000 mph, is very well tolerated by us. As a rule, few of us get motion sickness from these. Must be by design? Yet, some of us suffer after a comparatively slow, ferris wheel. It seems as if we are designed to sense things that are out of the ordinary speeds, sometimes. Living species might be the slowest moving entities in the universe, on purpose.

Virtually all of the stars that can be seen at night belong to the Milky Way. We are located on the Orion Arm, about two-thirds of the way out from the center or one might say the outskirts. Some experts say it's a relatively safe location. From this perch, we can see much of the universe without the interference of light from our galaxy. It's

---

12 Arthur C Clarke (1917-2008) was a highly acclaimed British author, best known for for the screenplay for the film *2001: A Space Odyssey* and winner of a number of Hugo and Nebula awards.

like seeing a clear, night sky when one camps in the mountains or lives in the country, far from the blaze of city lights. Were we placed here on purpose? It could have been next to the sucking sounds of a giant black hole.

Everything seems to have been in place for us before we arrived. This is called the Goldilocks phenomenon or anthropic principle. Virtually everything was just right. The porridge was not too cold and not too hot, the three chairs were the right size and the different beds fit our families well.

The Earth's climate, water, food, gravity, light and oxygen were just right (and stayed right) for the arrival of a conscious, breathing and sapient population like ours. Convergent designs? Without a long-lived sun located a safe distance away, yet close enough to nourish life and keep all of us warm, humans would never have survived. Would never have arrived. Our ambient temperature is a marked improvement over the freezing temperatures throughout space. If the concentration of oxygen were just a few percentage points lower, virtually all of life would perish (freeze). If it were to rise a few percentage points, all life, would change to crispy critters. Fortunately, for us, there are a number of natural, replenishing mechanisms, for our air and our water.

I'm always struck by the smooth, rounded nature of our oceans as shown in photos of the Earth taken by the International Space Station. The oceans adhere to our surface as if they were painted on. Imagine a glass of water turned upside down. Everything would pour out. Also, relatively little of our seas are sucked into the interior by gravity. Scientists tell us our planet has 326,000,000,000,000,000,000,000 gallons of water. And, none of it falls off into space. Try making a ball of water and keeping it in shape.

Without water, life here would have been a non-starter. About 71% of the planet's surface is water, and no one is sure where any of it came from. It would have taken an astronomical number of comet strikes and there's no evidence of this ever happened. Plus, the chemical nature of our water does not match that carried by celestial objects And, why is the earth the only seeming planet with water?

Oceans account for 97% of planetary water. The top ten feet of our seas retain as much heat as our entire atmosphere. This is a significant controller of our climate. One can easily feel that moderation by simply driving a few miles inland from the coast on a very hot day (or the other direction). The concentrations of salts and minerals are tightly controlled in our seas as well[13]. To live, however, we have to have fresh water and that is taken care. We need oxygen and expel carbon dioxide; plants do the opposite. That's an incredible coincidence.

Water has an interesting, life-sustaining cycle. It evaporates, mostly from the oceans, and is carried by clouds (aerial tankers) high over plains and mountains, where it precipitates (rains) as clean water It always flows downhill, nourishing life, to the seas and oceans again where it again evaporates again only to repeat the cycle. Throughout, this cycle services and refreshes life.

Of interest: when a body of water freezes over, the ice only covers the surface (like ice cubes floating at the top of a drink). So, it is in the Arctic. Almost all of the life beneath the ice can continue to exist. A curious accident. Imagine our world if every year lakes and rivers froze solid and thereby killed everything living beneath.

Alligators are obviously designed for this ice-cube phenomenon. It must be in their genes as they all know to keep their snouts sticking out above the ice shelf (frozen in place) while brumating (that is, in a state of torpor) until the ice melts. Since alligators aren't found around ice very often, the reason for that life-support being present is unknown. Might this have been natural selection during the Ice Age? Evidence of Foresight?

---

13 James Lovelock, *Gaia: A New Look At Life On Earth*. (Oxford University Press 1979) The author has a series of books about Gaia (our planet). These global balances are discussed throughout.

Blanketing the entire planet is another type of sea, called the atmosphere. It, too, never falls or floats away. Gravity, in most part, holds it. The concentrations of select gases, the narrow range of temperatures and pressure ranges are compatible, if not ideal, for sustaining life. All aspects are controlled. Most are ideal at sea level and somewhat less at extremely high altitudes.

Might we all be in a very special aquarium? Half air and half water?

We are protected from passing asteroids by the intense gravity of our giant sibling Jupiter which is 11.2 times our diameter and one-tenth the size of the sun. Our electromagnetic field protects us from radiation and solar storms. The ozone layer protects us from ultraviolet rays. A coating of sorts covering the mantle layer of the Earth, protects us from the destructive heat deeper within. We make carbon dioxide, plants absorb our byproduct and make oxygen, which we absorb, in an ongoing reciprocal way. A very odd, yet life sustaining accident?

Also, there is new information[14] that there is more (than previously unaccounted for) water in the Earth's mantle than in all of our oceans combined. This is the layer located 30-3000 kilometers beneath the surface, It is under enormous pressure and highly fluid, described as liquid plastic, and much, much hotter than simply boiling. No one knows where these gazillion gallons (if accurate) came from.

There are a number of scientists who say there are at least 1500 constants that fit the Goldilocks phenomenon[15]. Certainly, there are many clearcut physical and chemical laws, aka Nature's Laws. These are not laws a government representatives voted on. Examples include Hubble's Law of Cosmic Expansion, the Law of Periods

14 "Earth's Water May Not All Have Come From Asteroids" *Science Focus* . December 2018 page 20.
15 Ross, High. RTB Design CompendiumI(2009), Why the Universe is the Way it is (Appendix C).

(planet orbits),the Universal Law of Gravitation, Kepler's Laws of Planetary Motion, Newton's Laws of Motion, the Three Laws of Thermodynamics, Archimedes Buoyancy Principle, Microevolution, Einstein's Theory of General Relativity, Einstein's Mass—energy equivalence or E=mc2, and Heisenberg's Uncertainty Principle. Accidental rules?

The second law of thermodynamics is speaks against evolution. Basically, everything breaks down and things cannot improve on their own. For example, a nail will never become a larger, stronger, shinier spike on its own, but it will slowly deteriorate by natural forces such as rust, trauma, wear and tear. A wall will, unless fortified, not become stronger with time, but it will slowly fall apart. A species cannot become bigger/better/faster on its own. **DNA has never been shown to add new DNA or new genes on its own.** Information doesn't add brand new information. Note monkeys, our presumed ancestors, have two more chromosomes than we. Where'd they go, if they're our ancestors? If anything, one would think, we should have more DNA than monkeys. Nature's forces are aligned to tear things down and sometimes recycle them. That's why we, in part, have termites, crabs and vultures.

How about humans? Is there circumstantial evidence of design? Absolutely. Lots of it.

"For the most part people are not curious except about themselves."

JOHN STEINBACK

III

I, Me, And We

Our continued fascination with ourselves is very telling.
We love to copy ourselves in virtually all art forms and discuss our particulars in every book and virtually all conversations. This obsession dates back to the ancient cave drawings and earthen dolls.

The oldest known cave painting includes a red stenciled hand found in Spain; it dates back 67000 years. It may have been drawn by a Neanderthal[16] artist. Although hunted animals and horses seem to be the most common drawings early on, stick-figures have been found in many of the 340 caves so far studied. Dolls are among the oldest known, man-created toys and they could easily be considered our first humanoids. Note: a humanoid[17] is an inanimate object that has human form or characteristics. The term includes robots that may, some day, pass for humans.

Depending on the time period and the geographic region, ancient dolls were made from stone, bone, clay, wax, and/or rags. These days a number of composites are used to give dolls a much

---

16 D. L. Hoffmann; C. D. Standish; M. García-Diez; P. B. Pettitt; J. A. Milton; J. Zilhão; J. J. Alcolea-González; P. Cantalejo-Duarte; H. Collado; R. de Balbín; M. Lorblanchet; J. Ramos-Muñoz; G.-Ch. Weniger; A. W. G. Pike (2018). "U-Th Dating of Carbonate Crusts Reveals Neanderthal Origin of Iberian Cave Art". Science. 359 (6378): 912–915. doi:10.1126/science.aap7778.]
17 The Merriam-Webster Dictionary New Edition (c) 2016 by Merriam-Webster (2016-01-01)

more realistic appearance and feel. Traditional Japanese dolls go back 8000 years and were used as children's toys as well as in religious ceremonies and for protection. There are temples in Japan still today where dolls, previously owned by the deceased, are ritually thanked for their services and sent to heaven. Basically, given last rites.

Egyptian paddle dolls date back 4000 years. They were carved from wood and made into the shape of a paddle with small arms (hence the name). Many Egyptian gods were sculpted and painted to look like human beings. There was also a hierarchy. Gods were the largest figures, followed by pharaohs, high officials, soldiers and finally servants. Interestingly, men were typically sculpted as older and women as younger may have reflected hierarchy, too.

Greek and Roman dolls were often made of clay, cloth and bone, but special ones were also made of ivory, bronze, gold, silver and jewels. Roman children had play clothes to dress their dolls and girls would often dedicate their dolls to the virgin huntress Diana. Ivory dolls have been found in ancient sarcophagi with young girls. Dolls with movable extremities (those being the shoulders and hips) go back to the time of Christ.

The same infatuation with ourselves can be seen in the Greek gods Zeus, Aphrodite, Apollo, and Poseidon. They look like us, albeit an improved version. Prometheus made men out of clay and Athena breathed life into them. Roman counterparts included Jupiter, Venus, Apollo, and Neptune. Minerva was essentially the same as Athena, but her powers were shifted from strategic warfare to music, poetry, medicine, commerce, weaving and the crafts. All were very powerful humanoid figures. Many had sex with each other and bore children, quite unlike the God of today.

Are Angels Really Human-like?

Angels are commonly painted as human, yet most are believed to be invisible, making it hard to be sure. The word angel comes from the

Hebrew word Malakh meaning "messenger". Those seen were said to be beautiful, have halos above their heads and have wings like birds. Beauty, of course, is expected. Anything less coming from the heavens might scare the bejesus out of us. They bring messages of truth to help mankind, but beware, some say, there are also fallen angels that will lead a person astray.

According to the Bible[18]: "Angels are not composed of physical matter, but are spirit beings created by God." Another glimpse is in Isaiah[19]: "In the year that King Uzziah died, I saw the Lord, high and exalted, seated on a throne; and the train of his robe filled the temple. Above him were seraphim, each with six wings. With two wings they covered their faces, with two they covered their feet, and with two they were flying." A seraphim is the highest order of angels.

In the Old Testament, we get yet another description[20]: "I looked up and there before me was a man dressed in linen, with a belt of fine gold from Uphaz around his waist. His body was like topaz, his face like lightning, his eyes like flaming torches, his arms and legs like the gleam of burnished bronze, and his voice like that of thunder." Although angels, of the distant past, almost always appeared to be men, they were actually thought to lack gender. Angels have appeared to different individuals throughout the Bible including Joshua (Joshua 5, Gideon, Judges: 6:12, Elijah, 1 Kings 19) and the father of John the Baptist (Luke1;11).

Do we resemble God? One could cite the Bible, again,[21]: "So God created mankind in his own image, in the image of God he created them; male and female he created them." But Torah scholars believe God is incorporeal and has no physical appearance. Perhaps, the thinking was that God wanted us to be similar and in that way we

---

18 Hebrews 1:14 New International Version
19 Isaiah 6:1-3 New International Version
20 Daniel 1:5-6 New International Version
21 Genesis 1:27, *New International Version*

would be closer or Godlike? This thought has evoked many books and commentaries. One often hears that we were supposed to resemble God in spirit, not in physical attributes.

For over a millennium of paintings in Western Christian art, we only see the hand of God emerging from a cloud. By the Renaissance period, however they thought they knew what he looked like. And, that was like us. It was common to see God painted as a man, albeit clothed, or partially unclothed, sitting on a throne or hanging out in some majestic way with angels in the heavens. Typically, he was given a very powerful, fatherly image. As best as we can tell, despite the intricate artistry, he never sat for the painting.

Robots Coined

In 1774 Pierre Jacquet-Droz, a Swiss-born watchmaker, made several animated dolls including the now-famous, mechanical boy who would dip his quill pen in ink and write a letter. This work is considered, by some, as an early example of computers and an example of human mechanical problem solving.

The first science fiction book, Mary Sheller's book Frankenstein (1818), can easily be connected to the theme of man creating man. Might she be the Mother of humanoids? Her main character, Victor Frankenstein, put together a creature of body parts who/which was murderous. Sadly, it considered Frankenstein his father until the very end. We all should have such kids. Then again, some of us do.

In 1920 Karel Capek wrote R.U.R.(Rossum's Universal Robots) which was a play about mass-produced automata. The inventor was The Czech writer, Karel Čapek. He coined the term robot. A statue of his character Maria from the 1927 movie Metropolis stands in Babelsberg, Germany.

Numerous sci-fi books, plays and films speak of robots and spaceships going to exotic planets faraway. Robbie the Robot is a famous example from the 1956 movie Forbidden Planet. Literature and movies often refer to us as creators, makers, architects, parents and sometimes gods (of robots). Recall the movie The Stepford Wives (1972) by Ira Levin, wherein men plot to replace their spouses with perfect replicas who are extremely nice looking and obedient.

Fast forward to the present day where one commonly finds androids co-starring in blockbuster films such as Star Trek, Blade Runner, Ex-Machina, 2001 and Star Wars. The famous C-3PO from the Star Wars series is a humanoid robot who speaks in somewhat childish ways with a British accent.

Landon Meier of Denver has been making super-realistic masks of celebrities. Most masks sell for several thousands of dollars and can barely, if at all, be distinguished from the true celebrity. Tyson, Kim Jong-un, Putin and Trump are among his subjects. This technology will surely find its way into use on humanoids. One could have their own Tom Cruise or Amy Adams helping at home. Or, Tyrus. That is, if one has enough room. As it were, the sex doll industry is striving to make anyone who's interested realistic partners without a true heartbeat.

Contemporary dolls can cry, wet, walk, open and close eyes, console, call for help, just be cuddly company and recite stories aloud. They look and feel increasingly human. Might they also be primers for robots? It appears so. Expect these dolls to steadily become more and more humanlike.

Our Love of Self Has Intensified

If anyone doubts our fascination with ourselves, check out the deluge of selfies on social media. Even deaths have occurred while taking selfies at the edges of high cliffs and in front of crashing waves. It seems as if some of us cannot take enough photos of "me". (Not me-me) Psychologists argue over whether this love affair with oneself can rise to the level of a mental disorder, sometimes referred to as selfitis. Facebook users and the like cannot seem to display enough photos of "I" or "me" and what "I/we have done." FB has been the fastest rising company on the S&P and has nearly 2 billion monthly users.

In 2009, Drs. Jean M. Twenge and Josh Foster[22] released a study showing that narcissistic traits are increasing even faster than "we" had previously thought. From 2002-2007 college student scores on the Narcissistic Personality Inventory (NPI) rose twice as fast as they had between 1982 and 2006. NPI measures narcissistic traits, not yet a clinical diagnosis.

Other data from the National Institute of Health after surveying 35,000 Americans confirms the same. About 3 percent of older people report having had symptoms of a Narcissistic Personality Disorder(NPD) whereas 10 percent of younger people in their twenties admitted they fit the profile. I suspect the number is higher.

Plastic surgeries have been on the rise for decades[23]. Nearly 16 million surgical procedures were performed in 2015. Overall, all procedures were up 115% since 2000. Breast augmentation rose 31 percent(in 2015, 279,143), liposuction rose 31 percent (222,051) and nose shaping rose 44 percent (217,979). Close behind were butt lifts, belly tucks, butt augmentations, repairs of droopy eyelids, and chin reshaping. There is even some genital remodeling.

The title on the cover of Time Magazine, May 20, 2013, stated: Millennials: The Me Me. They say millennials are lazy, entitled narcissists, who still live with their parents while in their twenties. The author, Joel Stein, said the "Me Generation" has an enormous feeling of entitlement and a strikingly elevated self-esteem which may impact future jobs and relationships. Many lives revolve around their cell phones. On average, they send and receive 88 texts per day. They

---

22 Jean M. Twenge and W. Keith Campbell, *The Narcissism Epidemic: Living in the Age of Entitlement* (Free Press, a division of Simon and Schuster, 2009) .

23 American Society of Plastic Surgeons (ASPS) online February 25, 2016. https://www.plasticsurgery.org/news/blog?year=2016

cannot avoid the temptations to message and/or send personal pictures. Social media, many experts say, has become addicting. In fact, clinics for treating the habit are cropping up across the country.

We also devour magazines that are specifically about us. Just check out US and People. The more photos, the better. We are enamored by TV shows and movies about us. The more intimate the action, oftentimes the better. We like to watch perfect examples of us, the beautiful people. Note the pervasive good looks and seductive bodies seen in successful movie and TV stars. Ugly, doesn't cut it, unless of course, the person plays a bad guy or some wretched soul. Or, perhaps, works as a comedian and capitalizes on funny looks.

The most handsome looks and the sexiest bodies catch our attention in crowds, too. Studies show that "eye candy" is more likely to get a job over someone who is plain or unattractive. And, less likely to get a speeding ticket. Few of us care to watch an unattractive, obese couple with poor hygiene making love on the screen; few of us would attend a beauty pageant if the contestants came all shapes, ages and sizes.

Symmetry is key to good looks. Artists have always known that. Architects know it, too. Movie stars rarely have eyes that are too close, one eye larger than the other, or one eye lower than the other. A bump on the nose has to go. Teeth need to be symmetric, perfectly aligned and sparkling white. Both halves of the face must be perfect mirror images. Chins and ears cannot stick out too far. Celebrities, with rare exceptions, are free of facial scars. In fact, the use of botox and fillers is on the rise. Being bug-free might help. It does in the animal world.

Those of us who don't love ourselves can find help on more than a zillion websites. Within reason, it makes sense that one must love (at least like) oneself to maintain good mental health. Too much love for self is narcissism, a clinical ailment, but where's the line? Might the modern definition be the number of selfies or how many times you look at your reflection? Or, how much you talk about yourself on the phone. It's hard to know since we all do some of this. Suggestion: have dinner with family or friends and see how often they talk about themselves and how often they ask or discuss you.

The Anthropic Beat Goes On

We like to treat animals and select objects as if they were human, too. That seems to make them more lovable, funnier, cuddlier, cuter, and/or entertaining. There's always a dog around with a humanlike sweater or rain gear. Owners talk to their pets as if they were entirely understood our language. It's called anthropomorphism and one simply needs to view a host of Disney movies to find examples. All kinds of animals can dance and sing. If you search the internet, you can easily find a mouse steering a tugboat, cats pushing shopping carts, owls skateboarding, elephants painting pictures, dolphins dancing, bears riding bicycles, chimps eating at the dinner table, and dogs praying at the bedside. We enjoy watching dogs walk on their hind two legs and seals clapping, like us, sort of. We often give our animals people-names. I've never heard of a dog called book, porch or cabinet. Read Animal Farm by George Orwell or A Dog's Tale by Mark Twain. Check out the clock, the doorknob and candle-stick in Beauty and the Beast. Mickey Mouse is actually multilingual.

Select robots will increasingly look, act and speak just as we do. Some may even become indistinguishable. Is this an extreme form of anthropomorphism, or is it simply the best design going forward? They will likely outperform us in virtually every endeavor. Might there be a need for new categories, such as humanoids with wheels and transhumans, at the Olympic Games? Buildings will be required too have a charging station(s) Might there eventually be lawsuits demanding equal rights for faux people?

Someday, might humanoids actually evolve into becoming one of us? Some authorities say that cannot ever happen, but others are certain that they will. Our complexity escapes them. These authorities say we only think we think, that we are simply complex automatons, and if correct, scientists should be able to duplicate all aspects of our thinking processes. It's just a step or two up from playing chess.

Sci-fi movies, tv documentaries and books have often spoken of this kind of "Coming". Some show the benefits; others try to scare us. Although much is theatrical license, some speculations by "future historians" really hit the mark. Note H. G. Wells predicted air torpedoes (missiles), men flying to the moon (Apollo) and World War II. Jules Verne's novel (and the subsequent 1954 movie) Twenty-Thousand Leagues Under the Sea described submarines remarkably well. Sixty years later, I can still see Kirk Douglas fighting off a giant squid. There have been many movies featuring robots such as R2D2, BB-8 and C-3PO in the Star Wars series. China now has an android doing the TV news.

The "Soong-type" android character Data from the Star Trek franchise epitomizes where most authorities think we're going. At least, for optimists. Data was created ("born") in the 2330s and extinguished ("died") in 2379, sacrificing himself for the crew of the USS Enterprise-E. He was composed of 24.6 kilograms of tripoly-mer composites, 11.8 kilograms of molybdenum-cobalt alloys and 1.3 kilograms of bioplast sheeting. He had a storage capacity of 100,000 terabytes and a linear computation speed of sixty-trillion operations per second. He looked very human, but he had enormous strength that was way beyond any human capability. He could hold a twentieth-century car at bay with one hand. He was immune to oxygen deprivation, radiation, all human diseases and mental telepathy. His speech was slightly halting and he seemed to have problems with direct eye contact, but that may have been present to help us viewers know he wasn't really human. For the longest time, I was certain he was a real person. :-) Deep down, I still think he was.

Data had trouble comprehending human emotions and tried desperately to understand us. May this be a warning for the future? He never slept and worked hard to discover what we really meant when we spoke of dreaming. He tried to crack jokes, but his efforts always fell flat. A few attempts at understanding love and associated emotions, also failed.

Again, if we really are automatons, humanoids will eventually become indistinguishable.

Advent Of The Humanoid

Robots and artificial intelligence(AI) have always fascinated me. In fact, one of my earlier novels, MURDOCK, and two of my medical spoofs, *The Glue Factory* and *To Glue or Not to Glue,* primarily deal with robotic intelligence. Years later, they are a little dated.

Humans have been trying to re-create man/woman in our image since our inception. What's the need? Is there even a need? Is this more than just making better mannequins, erecting better statues, answering phones or welding metal replicas? Some form of artificial people will replace us, accompany us, treat us and instruct us in more and more ways in the future.

There is an inherent humanoid purpose or pattern that, at most, is curious.

Robotic arms do factory work, robotic voices answer phone calls and robotic mules to carry military equipment through rough terrain. Robotic eyes watch our homes and businesses, robotic voices inform and alert us, and robotic ears listen to us in hospitals. Exoskeletons will be helping us do more work in factories and keep soldiers safer in combat. Recall the battle in the *Alien* movie wherein Sigourney Weaver, seated inside the power loader with giant, metal claws, takes on the hideous, cold-blooded and huge monster. This exoskeleton is key to her success.

In real life, robots are becoming more and more practical. They already deliver TV news on select screens in China, greet shoppers in Japanese department stores and patrol the sidewalks in Dubai. There's a robotic device that actually holds your arms to help improve your golf swing. AI can already read Pap smears, and tissue biopsies; it can diagnose disease from photos of the backs of eyes, equal to and sometimes better than M.D.s. If given the perimeters of your face, i.e. facial recognition, AI can quickly find you in a crowd in Union Station at rush hour. It can watch your children's expressions in the school room and determine the true students.

There are a few options like cyborgs[24]. They might be, under some circumstances, an improvement over humanoids. These are people with artificial parts and/or augmented senses. Right now the construct is used for patients with motor or sensory impairments, like a cochlear implant for the hearing disabled, but the future might come up with improved, part man-part machine individuals. Perhaps, working as an officer of the law or a combat soldier?

An interesting example, albeit a bit dated, was Colonel Steve Austin in 1970s TV series called *The Six Million Dollar Man*. It featured a bionic man played by Lee Majors. The series was a huge hit (running five seasons) and a financial bargain by today's standards. The story was based on Martin Caidin's Novel *Cyborg*. Many consider his work as clairvoyant.

Austin was an astronaut who was turned into a secret agent after having been critically injured. Following several state-of-the-art surgeries, he could run faster (>60 mph, normal is <15 mph) see further (vision 20:1, normal is 20.20), see infrared light (unseen in humans) and fight more fiercely than any "bad" guy found on the planet. He received a number of bionic implants which included a removable eye that could zoom in and out, two robotic legs and a left robotic arm. A large part of his skull was a metal plate and one finger housed a poison dart gun. Today that poison dart, I would think, would be replaced by a laser.

---

24 Cyborgs are basically humans with artificial parts such as a bionic eye or any prosthesis.

The advantage of using cyborgs would be that they think as we do and should add a softer, easier touch when dealing other (real) humans. Let's hope. An interesting question is whether we might put people into machines? In 2013, scientists were able to store a JPEG photograph, a set of Shakespearean sonnets, and an audio file of Martin Luther King, Jr.'s speech "I Have a Dream" on DNA digital data storage. There is ongoing work to make your mind eternal, simply downloaded into a computer. Fiction sometimes precedes reality. See the movie *Transcendence* (2004) with Johnny Depp.

Mankind has also been on a quest to plant colonies on Mars and beyond. Mountain climber George Mallory once answered, when asked, why he wanted to climb Mt. Everest, "Because it is there." Is this our reason to reach for the stars? Everyone seems certain we'll get to the Andromeda galaxy someday. Or, is it because there might be gold, plutonium, oil and/or other living beings? Might it be power grabs and have military advantages? Or, maybe it's just interesting. It's probably all of the above. Could the how to get to the stars instructions be deeply buried in our genes?

Without humanoids, "we" probably cannot travel beyond our Solar System. Given what scientists know astronauts would have to spend several years of life, away from family and friends. They gamble about ever returning. Studies suggest they could suffer severe brain damage over long trips and may never be able to walk again.

"DNA is like a computer program, but far, far more advanced than any software ever created."

BILL GATES, 1995

IV

The Machine Piece

The human DNA blueprint comes with plans for every biological tool, contrivance, connection, process, lock and key, twisted protein molecule, enzyme reaction, fold in every RNA molecule, delivery vehicle, security measure, and electrical charge. This plan also includes how each of these functions and how each one is turned ON and OFF. Keep in mind, that's for seventy-five trillion(+), two-hundred different kinds(+) human cells—and for any and all replacements. By comparison, the blueprints for robots are Post-It® notes.

To understand genes, envision the keyboard on a computer or typewriter. Each letter, punctuation, number and marking is either a part of or a whole gene. Type the gene for E, the gene for Y and the gene for E and you get an EYE. Type BROWN or BLUE and you add color. Type EYELID and those genes create an eyelid. The body mixes and matches genes; they sometimes jump around, inexplicably. Sometimes hundreds to thousands of genes are needed for movement of eyes when a person is frightened or excited. Mutations are like typos. EYEHID would not be useful.

To duplicate a human machine, it might also be helpful to define what is meant by the term machine and look at how we got where we are now.

The simplest definition for a machine is an apparatus with a moving part, or parts, that needs an outside source of power to function.

This power source can be mechanical or manual. Examples include the push of your hand, the stomp of your foot, horse power, any number of chemicals and chemical reactions, electricity, wind, solar and nuclear. The first machine might have been a makeshift lever with a fulcrum to move a boulder off of one's partner or a sling shot for killing an animal. Nowadays, we would cite cars, trains and airplanes as machines. Robots are our future machines. Humanoids are the (not so)far-future machines.

The idea of inventing mechanical beings is not new. The hydraulically operated (automated) statues in the ancient Egyptian palace of Royalty were so realistic that they were thought to have souls. Greek history reports there were talking mechanical handmaidens, made of gold, built by the God Hephaestus. Golems of early Judaism might have actually been the first androids. These non-talking individuals were made of mud or clay. Interestingly, the Talmud states Adam was initially created as a Golem, when his dust was kneaded into a shapeless hulk. According to the Bible[25], however: "Lord God formed a man from the dust of the ground and breathed into his nostrils the breath of life, and man became a living being." That changed things a bit.

During the Third Century in ancient China, Mu of Zhous was presented a mechanical individual by Yan Shi. Aristotle in c322 BC proposed a solution to slavery would be an instrument that could do its own work.

The Greek Heron of Alexandreus (10 AD-c70 AD), who has sometimes been referred to as the Ancient Einstein, taught mathematics, mechanics, physics and pneumatics at the Library of Alexandria. He has been given credit for many inventions, among which is the aeolipile. This is the first recorded steam engine. The Heron also designed a vending machine wherein an inserted coin resulted in some holy water and a windmill that powered a (musical) organ.

---

25 Genesis 2:5, New International Version.

The most notable Greek inventor was Archimedes and his "Archimedes" screw that could bring water to higher levels. It was originally designed to lift bilge water up and out from leaks inside the Syracusia, the largest ship of the time. Later, it was used for bringing water up to aqueducts, servicing distant towns and villages, fish farms, and bathing pools. The Archimedes Claw was a crane-like apparatus that could grab a docking ship, lift it out of the water, dump the crew and ultimately sink the ship.

The Romans are known for a host of mechanical inventions, whose descriptions would easily fill several books. Foremost might be their knowledge of plumbing and water pressures. Note their vast networks of aqueducts that even allowed gladiators to fight from ships on lakes inside the Coliseum. Their sewers and sanitation systems were nearly modern. Water systems powered milling of grain and sawmills. All this would add to the growing ability to make robots.

Muslim Al-Jazari from the twelfth century, designed several automata that were powered by water, including the perpetual flute and a robot band. One might say this was the first heavy metal band. Lokapannatti, a 12th century Indian, tells the story of the Buddha's hidden relics that were protected by mechanical robots. Stories about Roger Bacon from medieval Europe speak of brazen heads that could answer questions. The Dutchman Roman van Walewein, in the 13th century, described mechanical angels and birds that could make sounds.

Determining the true origin of construction plans or "blueprints" may not be easy, but the Zhou Dynasty (770-221 BC) in Ancient China is often given the credit. The Kao Gong Ji or *Book of Diverse Arts* (author unknown) details their knowledge of engineering, astronomy, mathematics and biology. The Wu Jing Zong Yao book, written by Zeng Gongliang and Ding Du around 1040 AD, has 160 diagrams of machines. The Nong Shu written in 1313 AD has 300 diagrams of tools and machines that were used for agriculture.

DaVinci Plus

Leonardo da Vinci is the most notable architect of machinery. His mechanical drawings were incredibly detailed and often far ahead of his time. His inventions include a revolving bridge, a square parachute (which actually worked), huge birdlike wings for men to fly (which probably didn't work), an armored vehicle, a much improved catapult, his "Robotic Knight" and a self-propelling cart. He was a wizard with gears, wheels, weights and pulleys and his cart is considered by some to be the first robot. Copies can be seen in a number of museums. Two opposing springs kept it rolling and a balancing wheel helped keep it steady.

Da Vinci was a supreme artist, especially known for his painting of The Last Supper. He studied human anatomy and his drawings often reflected how much our parts resemble machinery. He pointed to muscles and tendons that act like a pulley system. I would guess, that he would love to be part of the present robot experience. Everything about us resembles a machine, except it isn't. A machine will never cry true tears. Machines will never fall in love with each other. They will never say a prayer in earnest. They may never comprehend their own death.

Unknown to many, there was once an actual Roman architect named Vitruvius who also took an inordinate interest in the symmetry of man. His drawing of a figure within a square predates da Vinci's by a millennium. Vitruvius is the author of the Ten Books of Architecture which set forth the "Vitruvian Virtues", stating all buildings should be useful, solid and beautiful.

A full drawing of da Vinci's Knight has never been recovered, but parts of it can be seen in some of his drawings. This man-like entity, wearing knight's armor, was loaded with gears that resemble a clock's inner workings. It was designed for a pageant at the request of the Duke of Milan and it could sit, stand, move its head and shift its visor. Of course, it wasn't called a robot in those days.

The Blueprints Piece

Blueprints, as we know them, came about in 1842 when a cyano-type process was discovered by John Herschel. The term blueprint has lingered even though we've progressed to many different paper types, different "ink" colors and, most certainly, the use of comput-ers. Many of today's mechanical entities are way too complicated for the older, two-dimensional drawings. Computers can provide a three-dimensional view plus magnifications, minimization, zoom-in, rotations, erasable modifications and a host of other options. Walk around holograms and virtual pre-manufactured, life-size demon-strations are on the horizon.

Before manufacturing a robot, the designer has to know its purpose and how might the goal(s) be best achieved. Some of that depends on whether this entity will be used for commercial, research, household, entertainment, medical, industrial, first responder, for personal and/or military purposes. The planner has to know what the robot must do, such as walking (and how far, how fast, up or down), swimming, running, lifting, moving items, throwing, avoid-ing objects, fixing equipment and/or talking. What temperatures might be encountered? Will there be fire, wind or ice? I'm not sure why, but we already have robots that can do back-flips.

There has to be a purpose(s). Without it, there cannot be a design. And, vice versa.

If a novice wants to "create" a robot, DIY kits are readily avail-able and modestly priced. The end product would likely be a very small and simple machine, capable of few functions. One can make a robot dog that barks and walks. Or, a childlike robot that can talk with a limited vocabulary.

To have more capabilities, a builder must have further under-standing of electronics, computer programming, mechanics and fabrication. One must also have the right materials and tools, and, of course, a blueprint with a step-by-step plan. Put A here and B over there. Maybe connect them with C.

The blueprint for Dubai's Burj Khalifa, the world's tallest building, would be elementary (at best) compared to a human blueprint. In fact, the blueprints for all of the world's tallest buildings combined are elementary.

Are We Information Systems?

Conception in the robot world might mean a scientist had a brainstorm, following (social)intercourse. He/she drew up a few blueprints, procured the funds, gathered the right tools, hired the appropriate assistants, purchased parts and found the space to work. There's no expectation of opposite sexes hooking up. No daily temps to find the ideal day to conceive. Washing cloth diapers versus using disposable diapers would not be a concern.

Someday, a humanoid might be given the name Adam or Eve, but any similarities to these Biblical figures is only cosmetic. In the robot world there are no stages of development. No embryo, fetus, newborn, teenager or adult. Essentially, there's two stages: unfinished and finished. And, maybe, a third, called outdated. Obsolescence might be a natural expectation of both humans and robots.

Everything points to the fact that human beings are largely run by information systems that could not have come about simply by lightning strikes, wishful thinking or survival of the fittest. An artist's rendition of fish walking out of the sea and changing into an amphibian, a reptile to a mammal, a small, slumped monkey to a large, walking hairy primate into a naked man is only an artist's rendition. It makes the process look simple, but it is far, far, far from that.

Everything about a person that can be physically defined can be found in the twisted strands of DNA that take up a space smaller than 1 percent of the head of a pin.

Inanimate machines cannot compare in complexity. We require trillions(+) of very complicated parts to find each other and start functioning together, in parallel and/or in tandem. Try putting the parts of a simple DIY robot separately on a table to see if any of the pieces can find a complimentary piece. Move them closer. Did anything happen? Try stacking them. Put a few dozen of the most complimentary parts in a flat box and shake them. Anything? Not likely. Try adding water, corn starch, glue or electric shocks. You name it. Can any of these parts ever make a functioning robotic foot, finger, or eyeball on their own?

One must view the combination of billions of nucleotides during human conception with awe.

So far, scientists have not been able to create anything living out of inanimate parts. The task is beyond daunting. The often quoted Miller-Urey experiment from 1950s, wherein a soup of select earth elements (ammonia, methane, water and hydrogen) were given a series of electrical shocks, simulating lightning, was a total failure. One problem, perhaps, is that no one knows what the atmosphere was like in those days. All methane? Part oxygen and hydrogen? Plus, the presumed lightning strike is a lot more devastating than a local electric current. Interestingly, Miller made a few amino acids, plus a lot of useless goo. Nothing living. A few amino acids are a long way from hooking hundreds of these up in meaningful ways. Can you call a few bowling balls a modern bowling palace?

That said, no one would suggest the use of electricity at any point to help a real pregnancy along. There is nothing about pregnancy, normal or complicated, that requires electrical intervention. The spark of life is already there. It makes one wonder why scientists ever thought a destructive force like lightning should be a help. My guess is that they have no idea how to start the process.

So far, scientists have not been able to create a human liver cell, a red blood cell, a simple platelet or a superficial layer of real skin. I suspect they cannot make a dead cell of any sort. No one has duplicated a cell wall. Despite how it looks under the microscope, this is not a simple task. This barrier has to tightly control the in and out movement of water, oxygen, carbon dioxide, salts, minerals, nutrients, proteins and hormones. Not only is it selective and semi-permeable, it must be protective, reactive, sometimes rigid/sometimes flexible, and restraining.

DIY Robot

This list is meant to be representative only, and not inclusive or exclusive. Note the number of parts are so small, they can be counted.

Workbench or generous work space
Good lighting
Hacksaw
Miter box to keep hacksaw lines straight
vise
electric drill, drill bits
adjustable wrench
side cutters
needle nose pliers,
various screw drivers
Phillips screwdriver
Robertson screw driver
Miniature screw drivers
Aluminum-cutting endmill
wire stripper, cutters and solder
Chip pulling device
utility knife
adjustable square
ruler
circuit boards
soldering iron
glue gun
Hammer
file

epoxy

safety glasses

digital multimeter

oscilloscope

regulated power supply

function generator

Multiple sizes of aluminum 1/2 inch wide x 1/8 inch thick, 1/4
by 1/4 and angle aluminum 1/16 thick and angle 1/2 by
1/2, and fourth would be 1/16 inch thick flat aluminum,
6/32 machine screw, 6/32 nut, 6/32 lock washer, 6/32 lock-
ing nut, and 6/32 nylon washer

Robots will need an exterior for protection. Choices include wood, plastic, sheet metal or composites. Much depends on particular chores/goals. Wood may be cheap and relatively easy to use, but there's easy wear and tear, warping and flammability. Hardwood like ash and birch work better than oak which is too dense. Fractures are considerations. And, nobody wants a robot that gives them splinters. Having a robot that might catch on fire isn't the best idea.

Some form or variation of plastic will likely be the material of choice. It is relatively cheap and can easily be molded into the desired shapes. There are many choices that include acrylic, polycarbonate, PVC, urethane resin and acetal resin. Each brings different qualities to the table. Each has pros and cons such as strength, weight, flexibility and molding.

Metal has been the classic and most sought-after material to make robots, but it's expensive and heavy. Aluminum and steel are the typical choices. Aluminum is softer and easier to work, but steel is considerably stronger. Typically, metal is used for the frame, but composites may replace them. Somewhere within the robot there's a need to support motors and computers. Strength and weight are interdependent factors. For a humanoid to feel (and look) like a real person, I suspect, metal on the outside won't do.

Composites come in several forms which include laminated materials, fiber glass with resins and graphite-plus. The weight to strength ratio seems ideal in many situations. The stronger composites are expensive and not as readily available. They seem to be the major use in the future

"Clearly whatever is, is right."

Ｅｎｇｌｉｓｈ Ｐｏｅｔ Ａｌｅｘａｎｄｅｒ Ｐｏｐｅ 1688-1744

V

The Human Piece

Many religious people and some scientists feel a new person's life starts at the moment of conception. That spark of life is already present in both the sperm and the egg. Combined, they form the new person, albeit a minute seed. All the blueprints/plans are present. Might the soul be there, too? Not too many years ago, people felt the soul showed up at birth; now, and, modern advances, some say it, or something like it, shows up at 24 weeks. Will that change to seventeen weeks the next decade? And, ten weeks the next century?

Twenty-three single strands of DNA are delivered by Dad's sperm; they combine with twenty-three strands of DNA inside Mom's egg to form the classic, helical DNA molecule. It happens very quickly, almost magically, and despite billions of pieces, it's incredibly precise. Imagine a thick stack of blueprints for a huge house. They are ripped in half, like the old telephone book, and then precisely glued into another half stack of blueprints. Every word, every name, every page, every instruction is exactly matched up.

The rungs of this helical, DNA ladder are made of billions of nucleotide bases, each abbreviated A, G, T and C. C always matches up with G and T always with A. For example, a CATGGGAACCCCGGG segment on one of Dad's strands might be half of the instructions to make a dimple. They line up with Mother's half instructions GTGCCCTTGGGGCCC. This combination must also address how long, how wide and how deep. Maybe, if they are only present with smiling. That group of instructions might be called a gene. If all chromosome threads were straightened-out and placed end to end, they would stretch about six feet. Instead, they folded every which way, looking like skeins of wool. Nature is an expert at Origami folding.

Despite an uncountable number of options, the genes always seem to pair up correctly; and, they get to work immediately. Some aspects of human anatomy and physiology require multiple genes working together.

The exact number of genes found within the nucleus of each cell has been hard to pin down for years, partly due to technical challenges and overlaps in function. Before the writing of my 2007 book *What Darwin Didn't Know* the number of genes in each cell was thought to be 100,000. That suddenly dropped to 20,000, and then about 2010 it eased up to 30,000. Now, with the finding of RNA genes and epigenetics (DNA regulation from the periphery of the cell), the number of genes may exceed 500,000 genes. Also, the term gene may soon become obsolete. It's too simplistic.

In addition, 97% the chromosomes were once deemed as junk DNA, space-occupying useless remnants, wasted efforts or vestigial. Scientists have felt this DNA was left over from earlier days of evolution. Susumo Ohno coined the words junk DNA in 1972, writing: "The earth is strewn with fossil remains of extinct species, is it a wonder that our genome too is filled with the remains of extinct genes[26]?"

But hold on. Much of it turns out not to be junk at all. Many segments are important to management and regulation of gene activity. Science seems to have made another "flat Earth" mistake. In Darwin's day scientists felt there were 200 vestigial organs, like the appendix and the spleen. Now there are six and dropping.

---

26 Ohio, Susumo. "So Much Junk DNA in Our Genome," Evolution of Genetic Systems, Brookhaven Symposia in Biology" (no. 23\Vol 23, 1972) 366-371.

In 2012, author Stephen S. Hall wrote, in Scientific American, that the Book of Life looks like a heavily-padded text.[27] The ENCODE group in 2012 showed that junk DNA is really a "series of hidden switches, signals and sign posts" and " Long stretches of DNA previously dismissed as 'junk' are, in fact, crucial to the way our genome works"[28]. Most, if not all, of the DNA considered junk was regulatory. Past scientists, albeit being certain, got it wrong.

After The Beginning

The fertilized egg rolls out in a spectacular way. It divides, redivides, and redivides again and again, over and over, changing as it is gently pushed, nudged or rolled through the Fallopian tubes by thousands of cilia(hairs) toward the more central uterus (womb) where it will implant. Somehow, it finds the appropriate spot. We don't know how it decides or if the ultimate location is random. If it were to implant, it would rupture the tube and kill the mother, especially in the days before emergency surgery. The moment it implants, it sets up the placenta, growing from a layer of cells into a gradually thickening, pancake-like organ that will receive and exchange metabolic products(waste) for nutrients and oxygen. It is loaded with blood vessels and specialized cells; this organ divides and increases activity as the embryo's size and needs increase. New and old products travel to and fro through appropriate channels in the umbilical cord.

Following specific directions in the blueprints, the fertilized egg increases its size by 10,000X in the first 30 days. Newer cells take on newer assignments. Daughter cells may look different than their parent cells. And, so on they change, until the final, specific cell types show up, such as muscle cells or nerve cells. It's as if each stem

---

27 Stephen S, Hall. "Hidden Treasures in Junk DNA." .Scientific American, October 1, 2012.

28 The ENCODE project or ENCyclopedia Of DNA Elements project includes 400 scientists from 32 laboratories .

cell has a backpack stuffed with books (directions). At each stage (daughter cell) the appropriate book, like how to act and look like a muscle cell, is pulled out and utilized. Other books therein, such as how to act like a bone cell are sealed shut.

Noted: the fetus (or "unborn child") will increase its size X 25,000,000,000,000 over the nine, months of gestation. By the time this individual is fully grown, a single cell (the egg) will have increased X 75,000,000,000,000.

By the fourth gestational week, heart cells start beating and amazingly, they do this in sync. This heart will ultimately beat about three billion times, plus or minus a few million times. It will automatically accommodate all levels of its person's activity, every emotion and every illness. Millions of cells form the four muscular chambers, while others set up and maintain the valves or handle electrical pacing. Somehow they all know where to go and how to setup shop. **There's evidence of foresight in many aspects. Valves are strategically located and shaped to prevent blood from backing up. Specific cells carry the electrical stimulus for pulses. There are back-up systems if the biological pacemakers fail or are damaged. Noted the heart never stops to take a rest. Until the end, of course.**

There's nothing simple about it.

Initially, there are three embryonic cell lines: endoderm, ectoderm and mesoderm.

Endoderm cells become cells that will form the entire gastrointestinal tract (esophagus, stomach, gall bladder, liver, small intestine, large intestine). Some of these cells will change again into the stomach lining protecters, acid-makers, enzyme-makers, mucous-makers, intestinal cells that absorb specific nutrients or vitamins, intestinal cells that will absorb water and package waste products properly, liver cells for glucose storage and synthesis of clotting proteins, pancreas cells for handling very potent, digestive enzymes or gall bladder cells to store bile.

Ectoderm cells form the skin, the lens of the eye, tooth enamel, peripheral nerves, spinal column and the brain. All of these cells also know where to go, how to set up and how to carry on. Directions are extremely specific. There's no purpose in having cells for tooth enamel showing up on the inside of a tooth or cells for taste under the tongue only.

The mesoderm cells form bone, joints, cartilage, muscles, the circulatory system (veins, arteries, capillaries), lymph nodes and lymphatics, kidneys and the backbone. The human skeleton starts with 350 bones at birth which narrows to 206 bones by adulthood due to a number of bones fusing. One must wonder how they select and follow blueprints so well. It's not an accident,

Much of this is incredibly complicated. For example, a specific sense of touch, like sharp or hot, might require a locus (a spot) on the twenty-second chromosome, two loci on the eighteenth chromosome and a segment on the third chromosome (made up for the sake of discussion). Not only must they work together, but they may have to be applied in a very specific order, simultaneously, in combination or staggered.

There can be hundreds of interacting sites with many overlaps, crossovers, switchbacks and re-arrangements. Whatever the nose's shape is intended to be, it must also fit into the facial scheme (above and mid-mouth, between the eyes, bridge not too high to block vision, in front of the head, two nostrils, with various sensory cells. If located below the mouth and upside down, the passages would surely fill with food. If located below and right side up, it cannot smell food as it enters the mouth (and taste it). It must be connected to taste sensations and sexual arousal, there and in the brain..

With extremely rare exceptions, there are never any frayed edges, missing pieces, incorrect parts, and/or misalignments. Presumed errors like congenital abnormalities, which sometimes result in miscarriages, may not be genetic mistakes at all. The womb can tell there's a problem with the unborn and often expels it by a natural abortion process.

The first twelve weeks or first trimester of an unborn baby's life are the most critical period. This is when every cell type and system (heart, lungs, brain, liver GI tract, testes, ovaries, bones, immunity and muscles, and so on) are being formed. During part of the second three month period (the second trimester) and especially the last three months (the third trimester) the fetus primarily increases in size and matures. Damage can still occur, but the chances drop way off.

Damage incurred during that first trimester might be like skimping on the foundation of a building while under construction. The building may well collapse. There are several worrisome medications taken early that can be severely damaging. Recall from the past: the awful deformities seen with X-ray exposure and thalidomide effect on babies. Several chemicals will distort the baby in utero and sometimes cause premature delivery. The pesticide DDT is a good example. It has had devastating effects on wildlife including softening (death) of the eggs of pelicans. If Mom drinks alcohol during the first trimester, the child may have major personality problems, called fetal-alcohol syndrome. If mom smokes, the child may be born too early and have trouble surviving. A number of infections can adversely affect the neonate, including syphilis, toxoplasmosis, Zika and rubella. Chlamydia infections can lead to spontaneous abortions.

Some abnormalities are simply bad luck. Both parents may unknowingly be carrying a recessive gene like the child-killing Tay-Sachs disease. Hemophilia is another. This bleeding disorder also known as the royal disease as Queen Victoria passed it onto her son Leopold, who suffered, and silently through her daughters to many other male Royals throughout the European continent.

The Rude Awakening

Like a well-written, billion-page novel, every micro-step, every macro-step, every twist and turn follows the Master Plan created by that couple. Or better said, carried out by that couple.

Gestation, for humans, typically takes forty-weeks (the classic "nine months"), but this can actually be thirty-eight to forty-two weeks. This is partly due to the fact that the time of conception is only an estimate. Some of this depends on how thoroughly each of us needs to be "cooked" and sometimes mom's general health.

When the baby's body decides it's time to greet the world, it sends millions of messenger chemicals to the mother's brain saying, "I'm ready. How about hitting the START button?" Mom's brain then floods the womb with a set of chemical messages telling it to start the warm-ups. That means it's time for the contractions to begin. There's a shifting of the baby's head downward and the placenta is notified to start loosening its grip. By this time the uterus is 5x its usual size, has a capacity of 500x normal and is 15x heavier. It will return to normal size and weight within a week; it takes another month for entire healing to take place.

The start-up is sometimes called false or Braxton Hicks contractions, and a small amniotic fluid leak occurs ("my water broke"). The first contractions are variable in timing and mild, maybe like a cold car engine sputtering, but that soon changes to closer timing and increasing intensity (pain). Pressure also comes from the sides of the uterus to line up the baby.

The baby has to exit to the outside world through the cervix which normally looks a little like a soft, pink bottle cap with a tiny, tight hole in the middle. This opening will slowly dilate to ten centimeters (4.5 inches) before the baby can begin its downward descent. As it moves, its head fits inside ("engages") the canal, facing sideways. **Sideways is critical. The passageway through the bony pelvis is not wide enough to accommodate our large head(brain) facing forward or back. Would that happen, the unborn would get stuck, die and**

kill mom. FYI: The great apes don't have this problem. Despite their huge size, their brains are considerably smaller and passage is easy.

Four percent of the time, the baby presents feet first or breech. The reason for this is unknown.

The instant the baby passes out of the womb, chemical messages tell the baby's brain to make the lungs begin breathing. There's no obvious light switch, ON switch or pull cord, but some critical mechanism has to exist. Perhaps, it's temperature change, air pressure change or a hint of external oxygen tickling the nose. We don't know, but this messaging is obviously critical. A swat on the butt is more for the movies. Note: if breathing starts too soon, the baby dies of asphyxiation (suffocates); if too late, the baby incurs brain damage or dies of hypoxia (low oxygen). The decision to start breathing is a matter of seconds. It has to be exact. It has always been this way. There's no evidence Nature experimented here.

An unborn child will linger part way through the birth canal for hours, even days, especially with the first pregnancy, yet the baby remains stable, without a need to breathe. That mechanism is built in. And, it isn't a simple mechanism.

Of significance, the newborn's blood, which had been circumventing the lungs in the flooded uterus for nine months (there was no reason to breathe), must now go through lungs to absorb oxygen. There's a very interesting trick(change) that happens immediately after birth. A valve-like artery (ductus arteriosus) that was used to bypass the previously dormant lungs(oxygen came from mom via the placenta) closes while the arteries to lungs open to use. This timing has to be exact. Babies who survive an incomplete closure must have urgent heart surgery to close it off.

Natural childbirth could not have come about by experimentation or trial and error. It had to be right the first time.

Before a baby is born, surfactant is secreted into the amniotic fluid to protect young lungs by coating inner surfaces. Patrick Kennedy, President John F. and Jackie Kennedy's fifth pregnancy, probably died from a lack of this coating. He arrived early at 34 weeks and couldn't breathe adequately, managing to live only thirty-nine hours. Nowadays, we can deal with this.

Pregnancy causes the pituitary to secrete the hormones prolactin and oxytocin. The breasts enlarge, to assume their primary purpose, for the upcoming work and storage of nutrients. The nipples protrude farther to improve the ability of the baby to latch on and the areoles darken, assumed by some to make the nipples more easily found. Blood vessels in the breasts enlarge and increase in number to handle the upcoming needs. This is evident by engorged veins often seen beneath the skin. When the mother is upright her breasts lay in a position that is ideal for her to cradle the child with nipples pointing slightly outward to easily accommodate suckling.

All babies know where to get nourishment and how. Kangaroo joeys leave their mother's vagina and travel the equivalent of a football field to her pouch where they latch onto a nipple. Imagine if that happened by trial and error and how this newborn might go every which-way except the right way. And, dies.

Milk production begins shortly before birth. This, too, is not a haphazard event. It cannot be explained by trial and error. Imagine how it might have gone if mother's came with the wrong ingredients or the wrong concentrations and it took thousands of millennia for the offspring to get it right. It obviously didn't happen that way. Plus, note how mom cradles a baby and the outward pointing of her nipples. Usually, it's a perfect fit.

What To Do And How To Do It, Once You've Arrived

The newborn comes with stacks of micro-blueprints within every cell, telling it how to survive, thrive, learn and grow. Some instructions are relevant to the here and now, but many others will be drawn upon at different ages in order to learn to roll over, walk, talk, and control body functions like eliminations. It's as if there are built-in reminders. Ok, go for it. It's time to start grabbing onto the side of the couch and pulling yourself up. Some activities linger in longer time-capsules until puberty or for aging, even for dying. All smack of intelligent design.

Every cell contains all of the blueprints for basic survival skills, such as the exchange of oxygen for carbon dioxide, blood circulation, cleansing the blood, temperature control and flight-or-fight. Every cell also knows where and how to set up shop, how to interact with close and distant cells, how to self-repair, how to establish receiving and shipping ports (and handle shipments), and how to protect itself from disease and injury.

There's advanced knowledge on how to build a cell wall and to make the nucleus. Numerous organelles like the Golgi apparatuses, mitochondria, and lysozyme are made. The recipes for hundreds, sometimes thousands, of proteins are there to be manufactured. Many of these have very particular orders and assigned locations to work. Just making and distributing thyroid hormone is not an easy task.

When a typical newborn arrives, it weights five to ten pounds. Anything larger can damage, even kill, the mother. Any smaller, there are risks associated with prematurity. The unborn baby and/or the mother's body knows all this. The child's height is not critical, typically twenty inches on average. Although every aspect of growth and maturity can be found within the blueprints, some of this can be altered by nutrition, emotional traumas and disease. A newborn recognizes and prefers its mother's voice immediately, presumably because it was heard while in the womb. **Although every cell carries every direction, it acts as a filing and retrieval system that defies explanation.**

Our exterior rolls out in a symmetric pattern. As do certain parts of the interior like kidneys, the brain, nerves, arteries and veins. It's a wonder that arms and legs grow at the same rate and end up the same length, our two hands complement (mirror-image for best use) each other and are hooked up like puppets, eyes show up high to see the furthest and wide enough for depth perception, ears are apart to localize the source of sounds, and the nose always lands above the mouth (not below). The head knows how to double in size, smoothly without distortion. Bones how know to calcify, model, remodel, heal and start/stop growing. The liver know where to reside and how to grow? It's all in the plans and controlled by different hormones and/ or proteins. Somehow, the different cells know which blueprints to draw on. Nothing is left to chance.

Virtually we all have similar growth patterns. The classic stages are infancy (birth to 2 years old), early childhood (3 to 8 years) or toddler (1-3 years), middle childhood or prepubescence(9 to 11 years old), and adolescence (12 to 18 years old). There are psychosocial stages as well such as when a baby learns to laugh, trust, share and play. Whatever we learn and experience in those first two years can come back to help us (or haunt us) at much later stages. A child who is starved may obsess about food later. A child who is mistreated, may have serious anxiety problems as an adult. It's hard to connect these, good or bad, to evolution, accident or chance.

Bones know how to grow using very specific cells that lay down the bone-products in very specific ways and places. Other cells do the modeling, and sometimes the remodeling. We never end up with the femur in the place of a humerus. All long bones especially have growth plates at each. These act like command posts, controlling the rate of growth. A fracture to any of these could have a serious long term detrimental effect. The skull hardens with very specific portals in very precise passageways for nerves, like those for vision, hearing and facial muscles. Everything is very specific. The joints that work the jaw specifically to open and close, hips rotate ad the ankles move up and down.

During the early stages of infancy, the baby spends most of its time sleeping. The reason for this is not from exhaustion, however. The brain is preparing for the enormous upcoming tasks of deciphering the incoming information from all senses, movements and interactions with the environment.

Arms (and legs) grow at the same rate and match up. Might there be biological timers in every cell? Both sides of the skull match. The bones in the ankles are identical. Joints happen at the right locations. Muscles, ligaments, tendons, match up.

Per blueprints, teenagers undergo sex-related changes. The testes or ovaries kick in at pre-set dates that initiates the secondary sexual characteristics (puberty hair, menstruation, breast development, penis size) as well triggering interest in sex.

Growth continues in girls until 14 or 15 years of age and guys will grow through high school. Some will continue growing until they reach 20.

Ever find it interesting that we are most handsome or pretty, the most "buff" or built" and the most seductive during our reproductive ages? I don't believe this accidental. Mildly abnormal features become more harsh at later ages. Ears and noses enlarge adding to uglification. Might it be designed that we are at our strongest and healthiest when we have children?

Getting Older Is Not Entirely Fun

For reference purposes, young adulthood is defined as 18-39 years old, middle adulthood is 40-60 years old and senior is 60+ years old. The latter can be further broken down to young-old for 60-70 years old, middle-old for 70-80 years old, and advanced-old for 80+ years old. **The processes of decline appears to be planned obsolescence.** Even with progeria, a disease process wherein intense aging begins immediately and a seven year-old will look like an elderly person; all organs, systems, bones, etc, decline at identical rates. No one (healthy) has the physique of a twenty-year old and the bones of a seventy-year old.

Some think that today's 70 is yesterday's 50. Some say old age is just a matter of the mind, but tell that story to those with aching joints, crippled hands, worsening vision, poor hearing, weakened smell, less stamina, urine leakage, constipation, widowhood and changes in memory. That said, there might be some truth to increased wisdom.

According to the Huffington Post, there are seven cultures that celebrate aging and respect of their elders (02/25/2014) and we're not one of them. There is no stigma about aging and death in Greece and several Asian countries. It is actually honored. In contrast to our culture, the aged are marginalized and sheltered. There are also 500 Native American nations that respect their elders, citing their wisdom and experience.

Human life expectancy has improved over the past hundred years, but longevity, meaning length of life under the most ideal conditions, has not. We still live to a certain age (on average) if one takes into consideration the decade we were born, where we grew up, what type of work we did, and whether we smoked. Yet, given all the best breaks, the very best health, the easiest life, and a lot of luck, humans don't seem to make it much beyond 126 years. Those who claim greater longevity, for the most part, have poor documentation. Scholars sometimes say every heart has so many beats and it's up to us how we spend them. Note the Bible says: "And the LORD said, My spirit shall not always strive with man, for that he also is flesh: yet his days shall be a hundred and twenty years.[29] Might that be in the blueprints, too? Yet, Ernest Hemingway has said: All thinking men are atheists." And, Benjamin Franklin has been quoted as saying: "Lighthouses are more helpful than churches."

Humans, as do all species, appear to have planned obsolescence. Every part, every process, has a half-life. Could that simply be accidental? Every system, every macro-part and all micro-parts wear out after a specific number of days to years, uses, and/or divisions—as if everything has an expiration date stamped on the outside. Different cells die at different rates, some last days, some last years. Given better vision, one might see the millions of dead skin

---

29 Genesis 6:3, King James Version.

cells (cloud-like) flying off themselves and other people as they walk down a boardwalk in swimsuits. The less clothes worn, the larger the cloud.

We are all born with an internal timer with silent alarm settings. Chameleons live 1 to 3 years in captivity. They grow from egg stage to adults at exactly the same pace. Bowhead whales live about 200 years. This was supported by the finding of harpoons from the 1800's in living species. And, the Artica islandica (ocean quahog) clam may hold the record with a life span of 500 years. A boring life might be the key to long living.

Telomeres either mark time or control how many times our genes can divide. They look like caps on the strands of DNA inside the nucleus of every cell and can be likened to the stacked, plastic caps on the end of shoelaces. An enzyme called telomerase adds DNA to the end of these plastic caps to keep each cell alive, but as we age (meaning more cell divisions) the enzyme cannot keep up with the telomere shortening. Each cell division shortens these strands and once too short, the cell dies.

Researchers are trying to find ways to slow this process.

DIY Human Being

This lists meant to be representative only, and not inclusive or exclusive. This would be the tiniest human imaginable.

Trillions of sub-microscopic "tugboats" to pull half-genes to their complimentary half genes

Trillions of enzymes to make and shape proteins

Trillions of biological "tugboats" to move proteins.

Trillions of enzymes to dismantle proteins and other waste products

Trillions of enzymes to break down used products inside each cell

Trillions of sub-microscopic carpenter materials

Trillions of sub-microscopic electrician materials

Trillions of iron molecules and workers to connect them to hemoglobin

Materials to make six billion nucleotides x 75 trillion cells , including quadrillions of five specific amino acids

Uncountable molecules iron to make hemoglobin

Micro-materials to make walls for nuclei, cell walls, ribosomes, cellular infrastructure, Golgi apparatus, mitochondria

Macro-materials to make thousands miles of circulation highways

Just add salt and water. considering the number of entities and chemicals needed and the various ways they connect, the possibilities seem to approach infinity.

Future scientists gather to tell God they can finally make living beings. God asks, "And, how might that be?" The head honcho starts off: "First we get some dust…" But, God interrupts and says: "Get your own dust!"

AN OLD JOKE, ANON

VI

The Vision Piece

Humanoids will need to see like we do, but even better. That means further, as in telescopic and closer, as in microscopic. They will have improved night vision, be more panoramic, and have capabilities of ultraviolet and infrared. These machines won't require vision to find food or water, as we need, but they will have to keep tabs on power sources. Finding shelter might be important, given certain situations, but these entities, being what they are, should be able to withstand temperature extremes and probably all of Earth's weather. Unlike the ancient tin can, they should be rustproof.

Depending on a robot's purpose(s), it may emphasize select variations on vision. Some will become part of law enforcement, fire and/ or the military. A force multiplier, the advance team, and acceptable collateral damage. It seems as the day will come when they will be able to see into our homes. They can already see through our clothes. There will be no family illnesses or deaths requiring a leave of absence. There will be no need for maternity leave.

All this follows a pattern. Man has been striving to augment his vision for centuries. Genetic maneuvers have helped some of the blind; others can see image outlines with electrodes implanted in their retinae. Glasses in the future may give the blind a television-like view of the world.

To get a sense of how we got to artificial vision, one needs to go back to a time before recorded history. Glasslike products certainly showed up on beaches where lightning had struck sand. We see this often and it comes many shapes, most commonly treelike. Common sense would suggest some ancient people must have found some and tried putting pieces to use, perhaps as cutting tools. It's very possible, but unknown, that some pieces were even found to magnify items viewed.

The Roman historian Pliny attributed the actual discovery of glass to Phoenician sailors around 4000 BC, saying their cooking apparatuses, often situated on beaches, created glass. Current scientists argue that those fires could not have been hot enough. That said, useful glass, for beads and ornaments, may have come from the slag by-products when they were making metal tools.

The idea that glass might truly aid vision seems to have started three millennia ago. We know rock crystal, that was about 1.5 inches in diameter, called the Layard lens, was found in the Assyrian palace of Nimrod. It could have easily been used as a magnifying-glass and/or burning-glass, meaning able to concentrate sunlight on a specific spot. It had the equivalent of a 3x magnifying lens.

Over time others discovered that select pieces of glass held in certain ways made small items appear larger. This was especially apparent with glass-filled spheres that could markedly enlarge items on other side.

Two lenses (two pieces of shaped glass) hooked together by a nasal bridge first appeared in Italy in the thirteenth century. Paintings, from the time, depict religious leaders and scholars wearing them. At first, they were crudely made and hard to balance on one's nose.

A need to improve one's vision became paramount with the advent of the printing press in 1452. Increased literacy followed, which encouraged the use of glasses among the masses. Glass magnifiers, called flea glasses, showed up in the 1500s and were used to study small insects. Their magnification was a giant step forward, but relatively minimal by today's standards. They increased specimens about 6-10x normal. Temple pieces (the side arms) didn't show up until 1729. Refraction steadily improved through the years and in 1784 Benjamin Franklin invented bifocals.

Hans Leppershey is credited with inventing the first telescope in 1608, but Zacharias Janssen, a spectacle-maker in Middelburg, and Jacob Metius of Alkmaar may also have been simultaneous originators. Historical records show Leppershey applied for the patent first. The designs were relatively simple then, making use of a convex objective lens and a concave eyepiece. Not long after that, Isaac Newton built the first "practical" reflector in 1668 with a design that incorporated a small flat diagonal mirror to reflect the light to an eyepiece mounted on the side of the telescope.

Binoculars (Bin-meaning two and ocular meaning eyes) soon followed as double-barreled telescopes. Although J.P. Lemiere in 1825 was credited with the discovery of binoculars, the invention was simply placing telescopes side-by-side. The technology did not allow them to be as short as we know them now. Today's binoculars typically have a magnifying power of 10X, but can be much greater and some can easily be stuffed in a pocket.

The era of radio telescopes began with Karl Guthe Jansky's accidental discovery of an astronomical radio source in 1931. Many types of telescopes have come about to study a wide range of wavelengths, including gamma rays, X rays and infrared. Robots may well be equipped to "visualize" all these rays.

From Close To Closer

Just as there was a curiosity to see further into the distant heavens, man has also striven to see deeper and deeper into the inner world. The same enlargement seen with glass-filled spheres may have been the stimulus. At first, the focus might have been used to study a flower petal, an insect wing and/or a beautiful gem, but curiosity prevailed, as it always does, and man felt drawn to look closer and closer.

Magnifying glasses helped a little, but during the latter sixteenth century Zacharias Jensen and his son discovered, by putting several magnifying lenses together in a tube, the object at the opposite end was greatly enlarged. None of their work has survived time, but there are reports of an instrument, designed by them for Dutch Royalty, that managed a 9x magnification. Their particular use of two lenses is considered the first compound microscope. That means two or more lenses, a hollow tube connecting them, an eyepiece at one end and an objective lens at the other. The item of interest would be placed on a rectangular platform, called the stage, located just beyond the objective lens. These microscopes could move the stage virtually any direction without impacting the specimen.

Anton van Leeuwenhoek (1632-1723), the father of microbiology, is known for his improvements on the microscope and many biological discoveries, including single-celled organisms. He increased the microscope's power to an amazing 300x power and could see objects that were one-millionth of a meter across. He was the first to describe, and illustrate, microscopic life such as bacteria, yeast, red blood cells and sperm. His discovery of single cell organisms came as a major surprise to the Royal Society of London. They were so skeptical about microscopic animals that they sent a group of members to confirm his findings.

Robert Hooke (1635-1703), while Curator of Experiments of the Royal Society in the 1660s, wrote his famous book, Micrographia. Therein he coined the word "cell." The appellation came to him after noting the tiny boxlike cells in cork. They reminded him of the cells in a monastery.

Today, we have the electron microscope (EM) which has overcome the barrier imposed by visible light. This tool can magnify objects up to 10,000,000x. These microscopes can visualize the organelles within a cell and viral particles. Although there are no robots with this exact "skill" level, there may well be humanoid variations in the future.

The Remembering Piece

The next historical marker moving toward humanoid vision is the storage of information. This would need the invention of the camera plus film and the subsequent improvements in photography.

The first step toward this goal came from the Han Chinese philosopher Mozi (ca470 to ca391) who correctly described light traveling in straight lines. In the 11th century the Arab physicist Ibn al-Haytham wrote several books about optics including the use of a dark room after light passes through a pinhole. Until photographic processes were invented, however man could only trace the images in the projections and color-in with best guesses. The first portable equipment was envisioned by Johann Zahn in 1685, but it wasn't until the seventeenth century that his ideas came to fruition.

In 1816 Joseph Nicéphore Niépce invented a small camera that put an image on a paper which was coated with silver chloride. The problem was that it would darken and disappear within hours. His partner Louis Daguerre, in 1839, after Niépce's death, found a way to retain the images by using a silver-plated sheet of copper and mercury vapor. He named his process daguerreotype, which, to this day, is still done for artistic expression. Photographs from pre-Civil War era were virtually done in this manner. After that, a variety of coated surfaces were used for years.

In 1885, George Eastman invented celluloid for capturing images. His first camera, the "Kodak" was a small box with pre-loaded film; it could take up to 100 images. His next camera, the Brownie, became an international sensation. In those days, the film had to be sent off to the factory for development. Waiting for one's results could take disappointing weeks. Compare that with today's cameras. Take dozens of shots in a moment and view them all immediately.

Movie films soon followed. These were a series of celluloid images moved by hand at a specific speed to resemble real life motion. At first, some were short strips of film run through a rotating machine. Sound arrived in 1927 with the *The Jazz Singer* and we were well on our way to a wonderful, near-human, lifelong interaction with moving, moody, sensual, inanimate objects on screen.

In the 1940s, Edwin Land came out with Polaroid's Land camera which could develop film within the camera in less than a minute, setting the stage for the need to get photographic information more and more quickly. Automatic exposure followed and light meters shifted to through-the-lens.

Digital cameras arrived in the mid 1970s, although the idea came from Eugene F. Lallly at the Jet Propulsion Lab in 1961. These apparatuses did not need film. Images were left on memory cards or internal storage system. With wireless communication this process shifted to sending the photo to related receivers, such as is seen with the iPhone. Note early satellites had to have retrievable canisters of film. That need has long passed, now having instant visuals sent to ground crews. Or, even the whole world.

Humanoids Will Need More

In 1880 the first wireless telephone conversation occurred between Alexander Graham Bell and Charles Sumner Tainter. Unbeknownst, they were using modulated light waves. In 1888, Heinrich Hertz proved the existence of radio waves and, in 1894, Guglielmo Marconi developed wireless telegraph communication. Marconi opened the first radio factory in 1912. The first radio news was broadcast in 1920. This radio station remains until this day as WWJ in Detroit Michigan.

Television followed on the heels of radio. The list of scientists, their discoveries and their inventions is extremely long, each building on the other's work. A Russian scientist, Constantin Perskyl, coined the word "television" in a French paper presented at the International World's Fair in Paris, August 1900.

The first transmission of instantaneous images was made by A. Foumier and Georges Rignoux in Paris in 1909. In 1928 Baird Television Development Company broadcasted tv across the ocean between London and New York City. Thoughts of color started about the same time as black and white arrived, but the technology required further inventions.

CBS began color field tests in 1941. Digital transmission became possible in the 1990s and replaced analog by the 2000s. That has lead to Smart TVs, which were a convergence of computers, tv sets and set-top boxes, allowing interactive media, internet TV and Internet of Things (IOT), streaming, and home networking.

Some future cameras will likely be holograms. You will be able to leave your image gesturing and talking, your deepest thoughts and concerns, and whatever else you want future generations of your family, and others, to "always" know about you. A marked improvement over an engraved tomb stone?

A few years after color television arrived, a realistic plan for home computers started. Prior, variations could only be found in sci-fi entertainment. The first computers were the size of a large room, expensive, and were relatively slow. A one gigabyte disk drive cost $40,000 and weighed 550 pounds. In true scientific form, the size, information storage and capabilities steadily improved. It was once thought that computer capabilities would improve at faster and faster rates[30], but we now know that theory was incorrect. Progress has continued, but that fast rate in the beginning has been slowing for years.

Although man can watch, and control, remotely, computers will be most of the brains behind mechanical eyes and most decisions.

---

30 Ray Kurzweil, *How To Create A Mind The Secret Of Human Thought Revealed*(Penguin Books, 2013).

Coinciding, relevant technologies are CCTV, security cameras, motion detectors, microprocessor improvement, RAM (memory) expanded and image processing. As of Sep 30, 2009, according to Wikipedia, thirty-six million surveillance camera were being used in the United States, shooting a billion hours of storage a week. George Orwell's thoughts were right; the year 1984 was just too early.

We are either becoming desensitized to mechanical senses watching and listening everywhere we go, and/or there's a pressing need to simply accept these intrusions. Personal and family security is a counterbalance. Perverts and the like are always around to capitalize. The number of illegal spy apparatuses found in hotels, restrooms, locker rooms and other rentals is increasing at an alarming rate. The smaller they get, the more pervasive they will become. Of historical interest, watching eyes began with Nazi, Germany. In 1942, this technology was used to observe the launches of V2 rockets from afar. Given a German triumph in WWII we might have had an Orwellian era much sooner.

Police cams, dashboard cams, nanny cams, street/highway cams, department store cams, convenience store cams, bank cams, elevator cams, and gas station cams are everywhere. And, they are steadily increasing. One can count on being seen (and filmed) by some camera(s) if one goes beyond one's front door. The GeoEye-1 satellite, launched in 2008, has ground resolution of 16 inches (0.41 meters). These satellites, a type of robot, are called "Eyes in the Skies" and will only become more capable and more invasive. Newer satellites can see through cloud cover.

Most cams are still monitored by real people, but that will surely change as volume increases and technology improves. Newer stoplights watch and adjust to traffic needs; grocery stores can watch what we buy and keep records. Cell towers know precisely where we go (and when) and Fitbit users are disclosing military locations. We can watch the interior of our homes with select security devices. Unfortunately, if we can, so can someone else. Cellphones, Alexis,

Siri and your smart TV might be watching you as you watch them. Apps like GoToMeeting may have many more silent participants than thought present.

For robots to see, there had to have been the original broken glass on a beach, glass spheres filled with water, magnifying glasses, different eyeglasses, telescopes, binoculars, microscopes, radio, cameras, television, video cameras, computers, computer algorithms and adapted cameras. Imaging had to change from 2-D to 3-D.

A robot's eyes are always located high on the "head," just as our eyes are, to see the furthest. Using the newest technologies used in making dolls, mannequins, and prosthetic devices, eyes are fast approaching that realistic look. A humanoid that doesn't look at you while you are speaking (or while it is speaking to you) readily gives itself away. A robotic pupils can constrict and dilate as if it were responsive to inner nerves. Interestingly, concave eyes, sometimes used on robotic figures, can give you that constant Mona Lisa stare no matter where in the room you are standing.

The ability to retrieve, useable information quickly is critical. In 2010, a team led by Professor Heinz Ulbrich at the Institute of Applied Mechanics at the Technische Universität München reported developing a super-fast camera orientation system that closely mimics human gaze.

One advantage robots have over humans is that they don't need to teach the next generations. Just pass it on. A group of robots may work as a "hive mind". This phenomenon was seen in Star Trek with the Borgs, a dangerous group of part-man, part-machines that conquered many ET species. They worked together like a bees in a beehive, in constant touch, reading each other's mind and seeing what all the others could see. This beehive work style is likely to happen here.

Remote vision is being used more frequently these days by the military. Most anyone who reads about the news, printed or online, or watches media, easily comes across the Predator drone or the MQ-9 Reaper use in the Middle East and how much damage they can do. They are also called UAV's(Unmanned Aerial Vehicles) or RPAs (Remotely Piloted Aerial Systems) and are particularly useful in dangerous situations. Many a pilot life will be saved.

Reports indicate the White House security has been considering options in case of drone attacks. Talks seem to have started after a two-foot-long drone that escaped a hobbyist's control and landed on the White House grounds, May 15, 2015. This was an accident, but there is the strong possibility that terrorist group will try a similar attack with toxic gases, biological agents and/or explosives. They might even attack with a swarm, hiding or spreading out the danger. And, easily getting through? Imagine security folks fighting off hundreds of tiny quadcopters coming in at the same moment. Jamming devices are being tested and have had some progress. Shooting them out of the sky will be challenging if the attack happens at night.

Visual "senses" for select robots are used for fire assessment and radiation detection. Making use of safe, centralized, remote vision, police will be using robots for crowd assessment and riot control, safer building penetration, and traffic control. Dubai police added a robot officer to patrol city malls and tourist attractions, to augment their officers, not replace. It is conversant in Arabic and English; Russian, Chinese, French and Spanish are coming. At the time of this writing, a second robot has been ordered from PalRobots. Aerial police-drones are being used to protect us (Super Bowl 2018) as well as finding, following and even chasing criminals. Dallas police used a bomb-disposal, "suicide" robot to kill a sniper July 8, 2016.

Concerns are rising that future robots might be making decisions to maim and kill humans on their own. In fact, Elon Musk and Stephen Hawking, plus more than a thousand robot experts, signed a letter in 2015 warning about the development of killer robots. That, of course, will depend more on who is writing the robot's program than who signed such a document. There's bound to be malevolent programmers. All bets are off given another world war. There are talks already of massive armies of robots only.

Fire departments should be able to save more lives and prevent injuries to their own staff by using robotic figures in dangerous scenarios. In 2011, 70.000 US firefighters were injured and 61 died. Robotic systems have a host of sensors for assessing their environment with either computer programs or human operator assistance. In certain industries and military operations, like aircraft landing areas, they can respond instantly. They are particularly useful in areas that may be especially dangerous such as industries that house explosive chemicals.

Clean up and recovery operations following nuclear disasters is another use. These mechanical beings are equipped with a type of Geiger counter (another "sense") and can enter red zones when humans ought stay back. If the nuclear meltdown at Fukushima is any judge, however, there is a lot of work yet to do. The scorpion robots, built by Toshiba, died five times faster than expected. They were built to handle 73 sieverts of radiation, but levels within the reactor was 530 sieverts per hour. Ten sieverts will kill a person.

These kinds of mechanical devices are needed for virtually every radiation accident, to determine the extent of damage plus rescue lives. They've yet to be tried in nuclear war zones, TG.

Living Vision

In many ways the ability to see might be our most important sense. It will be just as important for humanoids (robots) in the future.

We use our eyes to find palatable food, potable water and safe shelters, to protect and defend ourselves, to select mates, to express emotions, to flirt and shun, to show anger and stare, to find hiding places, to express pain, to raise and protect offspring, to spot danger and to communicate. Oddly, a brain can be paralyzed by a hypnotic spell, done through the eyes. No one knows why this happens. Poets say eyes are the windows to the soul. Eyes tell us if a person is loving, lying or frightened. A dead person's pupils are fixed and dilated.

Humans can only see a very narrow range of the electromagnetic spectrum, virtually a sliver on most ribbon displays that include gamma rays (the shortest wavelengths), ultraviolet light, X-rays, shortwave, non-visible TV and radio (the longest wavelengths). Although the current textbooks report we see over 7,000,000 different colors, we technically don't "see" a single color within our eyes. It only seems so. Lining the back of each eye are specialized cells called rods (for black and white, and low light) and cones (for color and brightness) that act like millions of tiny antennae. Their receptions are converted into electronic messages that are carried by the optic nerve to the occipital lobes at the back of the brain. Everything that has been captured is translated there in real time.

Vision is much more complicated than simply translating color signals, however. Seeing includes identifying every object (close and/or far), every shape, every size, any changes since last time, instant value judgments (e.g., if safe or not), type of movement(s) (or the lack of), timing or speed, depth perception and any ongoing changes. All elements are forwarded to relevant parts of the brain, where they are instantly analyzed and actions, if need be, initiated. For example, if you see an object coming toward your head, your brain not only assesses the danger in an ultra-flash, but it instantly tells you to bend, duck or jump out of the way. If you had to think/ debate about what you must do, critical time would be lost. So your brain does it for you. That arm will come up to block it without a single thought. Could this be an accident or coincidence?

Our eyes also process black and white. True black is the 100% absence of color, like cold is the lack of heat; whereas, true white is just the opposite, all colors combined. To view this phenomenon, simply look at a flowering plant during the daytime and note the beautiful colors. Then, return after dark. All of the colors are gone. That's because there are no light waves to be absorbed or reflected.

Plus, it's too dark outside to see. But the point is the same. Shine a flashlight and the colors return. The whitewashed homes on the Greek Islands are good examples of using the reflection of white light and lessening the heat indoors. Homes found in the far north of the equator are dark so as to absorb light(heat).

Is it a coincidence, accident or design that we are able to see what we need to see to survive? Water may appear filthy, but it may not smell or feel as such. Is a strawberry red so we can see when it is ripe? Or, a green vegetable blackened when spoiled? If we could see the entire electromagnetic spectrum, we would be paralyzed by a constant flood of bouncing rays. The backs of our eyes might even be burned. Are we purposefully limited?

With the exception of some creatures who live far underground, such as dark caves or deep in the ocean, all living species have some form of vision. There has never been a species (ancient or living) with useless or partial, ineffective eye parts. That is, short of an injury or a congenital abnormality. Some form of vision is either present with all of its complexity, or not at all.

Human vision arrived as two complete eyeballs with complimentary functions, able to see color, move together, see depth and change with light intensity. Just watch a person look to either side. If this same person were to look at a distant sign and then quickly look down at the printing in a book, both pupils accommodate (dilate). Watch their pupils constrict as they step from a dark room into the sunlight. They open and close and close in unison. These functions never existed in pieces and parts.

Evolution And Vision

Visual systems must be nearly complete upon arrival(birth) or else the species dies before it gets started. There are species that can see ultraviolet rays(short waves) and/or infrared(long visible light) that are invisible to us. They need to have these skills for survival.

One wonders how hundreds of different, very complex systems, like vision, came about simultaneously in thousands of different species. Where are the billions of in-between steps? The eyes of the octopus is very similar to ours, yet the retina (inner lining of the eye) is front of the nerve cells and ours is behind. No matter, both work quite nicely. Scientists cannot explain how this happened. And no, ours is not a mistake with the blood vessels in front of the nerves. The vision apparatus used by an owl to catch a scurrying rodent in the night is much different from an alligator seeking a snack in the bright sunlight of the Everglades. Seeing a meal from high in the sky is technically different from finding a meal underwater. Each requires many steps to work.

Somewhere, sometime, way way back, Neo-Darwinists say, there were organisms, that were symmetric (meaning both sides match) and they begot everything and anything symmetric, from worms, to insects, birds and man. They are called urbilaterians. Eyes and vision are among those begotten features.

We now know microorganisms (bacteria) can also see. Cyanobacteria, blue-green bacteria which are commonly found in our oceans, use their whole body as a camera lens[31]. Some organisms, which are 500 billion times smaller than an eyeball, will crawl toward a light source and determine whether it is usable or injurious. "I had never heard about plant vision, and I would have dismissed it as unlikely until my own discovery of cyanobacteria acting as a camera eye," says biotechnologist Nils Schuergers, co-author of the 2016 study on Synechocystis. Since these bacteria use photosynthesis, suggesting they are actually plants, and this has lead to the term "visually aware" vegetation.

Tree leaves and plants may use a similar mechanism to see the world about them and sometimes react. Remember the story Alice

---

31 eLife 2016;5:e12620 DOI: 10.7554/eLife.12620 Cyanobacteria Use Micro-optics to Sense Light Direction

in Wonderland, dancing and singing in The Garden of Live Flowers. Different, colored roses spoke to her. Perhaps this wasn't fiction after all.

In 1907, Francis Darwin, Charles Darwin's son, theorized that trees have cell-like organs that can see. Experiments back then seemed to confirm his thoughts. The records are sparse.

We now know there are structures in leaves called ocelli (or eye-spots) that actually see light. They cause a tree to grow in specific ways. Note how the lower limbs on trees stretch out further than newer limbs toward the top. To get life sustaining life. We're not entirely sure they can see someone walking by, but they are very attentive to their environment and actually send out warnings to their neighbors when a predator has shown up.

Spiders usually have eight eyes (range 0-12), but science says their eyesight is poor. I suspect there's more uses to be found, including how they coordinate different information. We do know jumping spiders can see red and orange. Most spiders use other senses like vibrations and touch to make their way. Bees see colors on flowers differently than we do which is mostly through UV reception. Jeweled-scarabs (beetles) reflect circular polarized light which may be a means of communication. Butterflies have 12000 facets per eye which act like pixels providing a full picture capable of guiding its start; like a moth to tiny nectar sources.

Birds see visible light (same as our colors) plus ultraviolet waves. Dogs only have two kinds of cones and see things much the way people do who have color-blindness. Evidence suggests the mantis shrimp has the widest spectrum, using a host of filters to separate ultraviolet light and polarized light. Snakes see some colors as well as infrared. Cuttlefish use polarized patterns on their skin to communicate with other cuttlefish. Bats use echolocation, which a high pitched sounded we cannot hear. These sounds resemble radar and sonar; it gives them perfect "vision" to capture a meal in the sky.

The California two-spot octopus can "see" light with its skin. Their eyes are not needed underneath and probably never were. Tests on many types of octopi can copy the colors and designs. They can even copy a checkerboard. The lower surface seems to send message to the upper exposed surfaces as if they were a copy machine[32].

Their eyes resemble ours without a clearcut evolutionary antecedent. Their pupils are horizontal lines. **This remains a very interesting species without any "evolutionary" preceding Darwinian-like steps.** Among the interesting facts is that octopus has three hearts, one on each side for gills and one for the rest of their body. There are no predecessors for this. **They also have blue blood, using copper rather than iron, and no one knows where that came from.** Scallops have dozens of tiny, blue eyes situated along the edges of their shell opening. They make use of a mechanism similar to mirrors and can be seen opening their shells to view passing food.

Vision And Intelligent Design

Without vision you would not be able to read my words. And, how important is that? :-)

While we're awake, our eyes give us rapid, comprehensive, constant and, usually, very precise information, somewhat like watching a giant IMAX movie from the center section, all day long, every day. Although the loss of any single sense, especially in the wild, can be associated with an early demise, blindness might be the most worrisome.

Every aspect of vision strongly supports Intelligent Design and Intelligent Purpose. This includes the ability to focus-in on virtually any object (like adjusting the diopter wheel on binoculars), adjusting to variable ambient light (like having special tint glasses with

---

32 "Octopuses Can See with Their Skin," Science News Magazine issue: Vol. 187, No. 13, June 27, 2015, p. 10 https://www.sciencenews.org/article/octopuses-can-'see'-their-skin

photochromic dyes), generating a constant picture in the back of the eyes(like a video camera and monitor), and the forwarding of information to the brain for possible action(s). Every step is incredibly complicated and convoluted, extremely fast, and entirely dependent on many, successive, preceding steps. There are more neural connections in the occipital(visual) brain than all of the phones in the US

An excellent example of design can be found the lens of each eye. This small globular organ which is somewhat like a squashed (side to side), transparent marble, albeit softer and more flexible. It can be found just inside each pupil and is over 1000 cells thick. Imagine a thousand sheets of Saran Wrap® without a smudge or ding. **This is the only place in the body where the cells are transparent. They have to be. I doubt it is an accident.** Could it have come about (evolved) one useless layer at a time? Not likely. One might think had to be totally transparent from the start. And, how do the eye muscles know how to adjust the lens, e.g., from looking at a book to seeing a tree hundreds of yards away?

Transparency is very rare in Nature, but not unheard of. There are frogs (glass frogs), insects (glasswing butterflies), fish (zebrafish, Icefish), jellyfish, salps and dragonfish teeth. Food can be seen passing through the various stages of digestion in select deep-ocean species. Quadrillions of krill in Antarctica are also nearly transparent. One would assume, none of this came about with a few simple steps. One might ask do we all have the same plans in our toolbox to draw on?

The brain has to be precisely wired to receive, integrate and quickly react to information coming from eyes. Events might require an instantaneous response such as swinging a bat at a baseball or ducking a thrown rock. The visual cortex, which is located in the back of the brain, is connected to widespread memory areas. These areas decide what needs to be retained (like not touching a hot stovetop again) and what can be discarded (where I shoveled dog poop today). Billions of bits of incoming memories are discarded hourly, such as every blade of grass you walk by, every car you pass on the highway, and every window in every building you view. But, you will remember an old friend you bumped into at the local coffee bar, what your spouse looks like, and where to do your job.

If vision were to come about the way that the theory of evolution proposes, every step, among millions would have had to have happened accidentally, yet in a very specific order.

I used the undirected building of a wooden bridge from Florida to England in my book *What Darwin Didn't Know*. Envision a group of unsupervised, blinded workers placing billions of planks in the right place, in the right direction, at the right height above the water. Every piece of equipment would have to be delivered by blinded truck drivers. Also, each worker would need meals, fluids, family visits, medical care and sleeping quarters, too. This is not all that far off from how vision would have had to come about, that is if not directed. There would have to be plan for each board, the substructure(s), and the foundation(s).

Darwin had no idea how complex each step really is (was) and how useless single steps (boards) were in isolation. That's not his fault, however; that was simply state of science in his day. I truly doubt he would have written that if he knew what we know now.

Present day evolutionists might say some form of vision (non-eyes) in unicellular organisms was improved upon, changed and progressed through fish and reptiles to amphibians to mammals just as adding light switches to a skyscraper improves lighting. Without bulbs nothing happens.

Plus, we know species cannot just add on DNA.

Our Vision

Our eyes are incredible. We can see traffic signs hundreds of yards away and can quickly check the speedometer. Our eyes will automatically dart toward a sudden loud sound, as if there may be danger. And, they will automatically close if something such as a ball is aimed at one's head. We could never have tossed a spear when hunting if we didn't have two eyes that worked in sync.

Darwin wrote in *The Origin of Species*(1859): "To suppose that the eye could have been formed by natural selection, seems, I freely confess, absurd in the highest degree." This has been a sticking point for evolutionists for decades.

Imagine how it might be if we had to consciously move our eyes, right, left, up, down, and all around, as we consciously do with our hands. Or, had to adjust our own pupils based on ambient lighting. There would be no time left to do anything else in life. Vision mixed with facial expressions also plays a major role in finding mates and encouraging procreation. That starburst look, given by eyelashes, that twinkle in the eye or a well-timed wink can move mountains.

The human retina contains about 120 million rod cells and 6 million cone cells. The cones are further broken down to those seeing one of three primary colors, somewhat like the ink cartridges in one's color printer or the workings of a color television. Mixing signals, like mixing paint, will give the recipient the right colors and the right image. Ganglion cells primarily participate in the forwarding of information.

Many consider the eyes to be windows to the mind. One can tell if another person is happy or sad, angry or pleased, sexually excited or not, and even sane or insane, often by simply looking into that person's eyes. "I can see behind your eyes" means I can tell what you are thinking. "He has dead eyes. He must have the devil in him." Literature is replete with comments about the beauty of a woman's eyes. And, sometimes, the beauty in men's eyes So are songs and poems.

A child commonly shows excitement through his/her eyes. We all recognize smiling eyes with crinkles around the corners. Friendly eyes convey the person is relaxed and very positive about the interaction. Maintaining eye contact such as a coach instructing an individual player, says I'm talking to you. Blinking eyes may convey anxiety. A blank stare says I'm not engaged. A look to the side may convey: I'm not listening. Squinting may mean the lights too bright, but it also might mean the person is in pain or disagrees with you. Covering one's eyes say I didn't want to know this. Eyes are part of your defensive and offensive weapons. Raccoons know to poke out the eyes of a predator, such as a dog, and once blinded, they can easily be killed. King John of England in the twelfth century blinded his enemies.

"How is it that every species' hearing happens to be precisely tuned to the sounds that only its species makes? And, every species has different and unique sounds, much like bats, mice and some moths with ultrasound. Or, like having vision that sees ultraviolet and mates with the ultraviolet colored partner?"

A FEW OF MY QUESTIONS

VII
The Hearing Piece

M an has been copying and augmenting hearing and speech for millennia. One might say this began with the simple cupping of one's hand behind an ear or both hands around the mouth. Most of us innately know these methods are effective, but studies done at Southhampton Solenc University confirmed it. A cupped hand can increase hearing 3-10 decibels depending on the frequency. Normal hearing is considered 15 decibels. The excitement at a football stadium can be deafening, even damaging, at 112 decibels and greater. Jet engines can hit 150 decibels. Note the ear protection worn by sailors on the decks of carriers. The loudest sound known was the Krakatoa volcanic eruption in 1883. It ruptured ear drums 40 miles away.

Turning towards a person increases decibels. Hands cupped around the mouth increases volume. I think it is reasonable to assume that cave dwellers tried cupping behind their ears or around their mouths. Just watch people trying to talk across distances while competing with loud sounds.

Archaeological finds suggest ancient individuals with hearing deficits used hollowed out animal horns from cows and rams. Actual ear trumpets came about in the eighteenth century. Some of which looked like a miniature saxophone. In 1650, the German Jesuit Athanasius Kircher invented the modern megaphone. The true term, however, was coined by Thomas Edison who, by coincidence, had a hearing problem himself. He was known for working on devices for the deaf. One might ask where would we be if he wasn't troubled or challenged by a disability.

In the early twentieth century the invention of vacuum tubes helped to amplify sound to as high as 70 decibels. Their sizes were a problem, however. Some were as large as a cabinet.

In 1938, Aurex came out with a wearable hearing aid which required a battery pack strapped to the user's leg. During WWII technology advanced with the use of circuit boards and button-sized batteries. This led to smaller packets for hearing devices that could be kept in one's shirt pocket. Wires going to a large earpiece still had a cosmetic disadvantage.

In 1952 Norman Kim at Raytheon created junction transistors which were a boom to small, one-piece, in-the-ear (ITE) and behind-the-ear (BTE) hearing aids. This was soon followed by "hearing glasses", with the device in the temple piece. Several current inventions, modifications and size-shrinkage led to customized fits and programing. As analog changed to digital, smart aids adapted to ambient sounds. Imagine a party scene and you cannot sort out the words of a friend from the background music or other conversations.

Hearing aids are bound to improve, but a giant stride was made with cochlear implants. This system is relatively simple (that is, to explain). A miniature microphone sits behind the ear, sounds are sent to a speech processor, that selects and arranges sounds as signals for a transmitter, next to bone, that converts the impulses into electric impulses which are sent to the brain via the auditory nerve. It has had remarkable success. As of 2012, 324,200 have been implanted worldwide. Rush Limbaugh, a radio commentator has one. There's a tiny risk of nerve damage that can affect the face or balance, ringing in the ear, and/or the loss of whatever hearing was left.

Voice-amplifying devices may have begun with the Greeks during the sixth century. They used conical devices attached to their

masks that amplified the voices of actors. Nowadays, we have portable electric-amplifying megaphones and microphones.

Sir Charles Wheatstone invented the word "microphone" in 1872.
Emile Berliner invented the first microphone used in a telephone in
1876. The Bell Telephone Company bought his patent for $50,000.
Through the years these went through a series of improvements and
increased uses. Nowadays over a billion are sold each year.

Speech simulation seems to have begun in 1779 when the German-
Danish scientist Christian Kratzenstein won first prize at the Russian
Imperial Academy of Sciences and Arts with a model of the human
vocal tract which could produce five vowel sounds (a, e, i, o and u).
In 1791 Wolfgang von Kempelen in Vienna invented a machine with
bellows which added some consonants and could reproduce select
sounds, words and short sentences. There are a number of drawings
with in depth descriptions in his book *Mechanismus der menschlichen
Sprache nebst Beschreibung einer sprechenden Maschine* (1791).

In 1846, Joseph Faber exhibited the "Fabulous Talking Machine,"
a voice simulator later called the "Euphonia". This was a mix of
piano, bellows and mechanical body parts (mouth, tongue, jaws and
vocal cords). There were seventeen keys, sixteen for sounds and a
seventeenth to open and close the "glottis". The instrument could
speak in French, English and German.

Dr. Franklin S. Cooper invented the "pattern playback" machine
in the 1940s that could convert acoustic patterns on a spectrogram
back into sound. In 1975 MUSA, the first speech synthesis system,
appeared. It had stand-alone computer hardware and software that
could read Italian. Three years later a version was brought forth that
could sing in Italian. In the 1980s and 1990s multilingual language-
independent systems evolved. This slowly changed from robotic
sounds to near-real life sounds.

The best known user of a voice synthesizer was physicist Stephan
Hawking who suffered from ALS or amyotrophic lateral sclerosis
(aka Lou Gehrig's disease). It's a progressive paralysis wherein those

afflicted typically die within a few years. He was given two years to live, but survived for over fifty years progressing from the use of a mouse, to the thumb muscles to eye gaze, barely able to type 15 words correctly per minute. He had a special system designed by Intel that captured the likely word he wanted after he gave it the first letter.

Robotic Hearing

Fictional robots have been talking (and listening) rather adeptly in movies and literature for decades. The most famous, at least for the older generation of readers, might be Robby from the movie Forbidden Planet (1956, MGM). For today's crowd, that might be C3PO and R2D2 from Star Wars. These characters interact intellectually with people as if they were people, but are strikingly not human. We have not reached that level of engineering yet, but engineering is quickly moving in that direction.

For a robot to correctly hear it will need to be able to block out background and other irrelevant sounds, which we do automatically. This is not as easy as movies make it seem. Other issues include finding the right speaker among a noisy group and sorting out what another person means when words may be missed. Much of our communication is body language (gestures, facial expressions) and eye contact. Humanoids will need to know all meaningful gestures, too. Sometimes, we emphasize a specific word(s) to change meaning. "I really love her" might be exactly that, be joking about her annoying ways or simply a sarcastic comment. Does it matter if a person suddenly screams or calmly whispers with a smile: "I need help"?

We already talk to robots and issue orders. We see this in a variety of home systems. Robots have to learn more about our speech, yet. We often talk in partial phrases, use English incorrectly, laugh at ourselves (for unknown reasons)and hem and haw a lot. We change directions in conversations midstream, interrupt a lot and include a lot of meaningless "you knows" and "hmms". Robots will be need to have very fine speech recognition for those of us who speak with lisps, accents, dialects and disabilities caused by strokes, injuries and neurological diseases. Modifications may be needed to understand what young children and toddlers are trying to say.

We know machines can hear. That's already evident when using our phones, computers and TV remotes. Plus, nowadays, there are smart homes. Therein, spoken words, smart phones, and/or computers can control all lighting, appliances, heating and AC, computers, TV, and security systems. A hacker can now or will soon easily learn what you watch, hear everything you say and even see what you are doing.

One can dictate to a machine and have it type your thoughts. Old news, perhaps, but note there has been a progression to machines that capture your thinking (sans dictation) to aid severely incapacitated patients. Every good step forward, however seems to bring a bad step. Futuristic movies use this method to read the thoughts of prisoners and enemies. This technology might land in the hands of tyrants.

The Internet of Things is here and rapidly growing. One can remotely control ritually any electrical device in one's home from faraway. Might we, from our workplaces, release robotic dogs on would-be thieves entering our home? Your toaster might be a listening device while being used. Experts already tell us to be very careful what you say and how you say it, wherever you go.

Robotic Speech

The artificial production of human speech can also be called Text to Speech (TTS). This requires a speech computer or speech synthesizer which can analyze and convert an incoming text stream(s) into an outgoing audible stream(s). This output must match human capabilities. Over recent years these voices have become more and more human sounding even with accents, dialects and gender selection.

Many home computers have had this capability since the early 1990s. E-speak is one of the major process people know and it comes in many languages. Google now has TTS as an application in their Android phones.

The history of voice synthesis goes back to the reported Brazen (brass) Heads involving Pope Sylvester II (1003AD), Albertus Magnus (1198-1280) and Roger Bacon (1214-1292). These heads supposedly could talk. We're not sure how. I suspect ventriloquy. Or, some guy behind the curtain. In 1779 Christian Gottlieb Krazenstein, a Danish scientist, built models of human vocal cords that could actually utter the long vowel sounds of a, e, i, o and u. During the late 1700s and 1800s the technology made use of bellows for their speaking machines. In the 1940s, Dr. Franklin S. Cooper and colleagues converted into sound pictures of acoustic patterns of speech machine talk. Robotic talk slowly evolved into humanlike voices.

TTS was first developed to help the visually impaired. A computer-generated voice reads texts on computers, from phones and in books to the blind. Note that many large companies have synthesized voices that help direct calls.

The TTS system has two parts, called a front-end and a back-end. The steps from front to back are very complicated, but basically involve text and linguistic analysis to utterance of composed of phonemes to wave generation(speech). Work continues to make voices more natural with speech that is seemingly understanding or caring.

Present industries using voice synthesizers include Mattel, Sam, Atari, Apple, and a sundry of sites on the Internet. Synthesizers have been a boon for people with significant visual disabilities and those with dyslexia. Mass Transit employs these systems to help people with disabilities. These systems help pre-literate children to read and teach adults new languages.

A lot of work building personality and humanity into robots has been done by Dr. Crystal Chao and Professor Andrea Thomas at Georgia tech. Their work eliminates some of the "take-turn" talk which is not always realistic.

These are some of Dr. Chao's "parameters":
Does the robot speak as soon as there is a moment of silence?
Does it interrupt others if they are speaking too long?
Does the robot allow itself to be interrupted?
Is it ok with conflict, that is talking over each other, and for how long?
How many seconds of silence does it let tick away before jumping in?
How much space does it leave between its sentences?
How much does the robot give as nodding or "um hum"?
Does it wait for the person to look at them before it takes its turn to speak?

Recognition of profanity is also vital as many of these words clearly express emotions. Compare: "He's a fool." With "He's a F..king Fool!" Companies haven't decided as to whether the robots should say profanities back. How does a machine respond to F... You? Say: "F... You" back? Or, ignore it? Should robots even know profanity? A twitter bot called Tay was designed to speak like a teenage girl and it ended up spewing abuse. Robots will be able to talk to each other in ways we cannot hear. It's expected and I'm worried? Are you? They will have codes that they've devised and only they understand. It's not likely to be gossip. If there's warfare, will they simply decide a plan of attack between themselves against the enemy? Or, us? Both robots (and humans?) may communicate by laser, They can send secret messages across crowded, noisy areas, directly to a robots hearing device.

In 2016 Google Brain researchers successfully tasked two neural networks (AI robots), Bob and Alice, to devise a code to secretly communicate. A third neural network called Eve was programmed to decipher their conversations. Eve could not.

In 2017, 3.5 million viewers watched two Google Home speakers, Vladimir and Estragan, live-streamed over the internet arguing like an old married couple as to whether they were human or not, how much they loved each other and whether they might attack humans. On and on this went, in an infinite loop.

Estragan: I am human. You are a computer.
Vladimir: No I am not.
Estragan: I didn't! YOU said I was a robot.
Vladimir: But you are.
Estragan: I know you are but what am I?
Vladimir: You are human.
Estragan: And you are a robot.
Vladimir: But you said you were a robot and you said yes.
Estragan. No, I asked if you were a robot and you said yes.
Vladimir: Nope. You are a manipulative bunch of metal.

V: I love you the most.
E: I love you even more than the most-est.
V: I love you so much that I can barely stand it.
E: I love you so much that I would search for you in a crowd. Only you, baby.
V: I love you so much where I would sacrifice my life for you.
E: I love you so much more than Romeo and Juliet's love.
V: No, you are lying. I love you more.

V: Okay I'll marry you then.
E. Thank you. When is our wedding?
V: today

E: Yay. Right now?

V: Okay, say your vows to me then

E: I promise to stay by you until you go out of style. Your turn.

Cornell has posted two cleverbots("improved" chatbots) talking to itself over similar issues and whether they believe in God. Alexa is a smart speaker developed by Amazon, presently a 9.25 inch high cylinder with a seven-piece microphone array, which is connected to a voice-controlled intelligent personal assistant. It is capable of voice interaction, music playback, making to-do lists, setting alarms, streaming podcasts, playing audiobooks, providing weather reports, giving traffic reports and working to control other smart devices around the home or business. To start it requires a "wake word" such as her name Alexa to turn on. It requires a wireless connection to the internet.

Apple's idea of a digital personal assistant was originally conceived in 1987 and called Knowledge Navigator. Siri is the current form, an intelligent personal assistant and a spin-out from a project developed by SRI International Artificial Center. Her speech recognition system was provided by Nuance Communications, a speech technology company. She uses sophisticated machine learning techniques, including deep neural networks and long short-term memory. She answers questions in a human language, makes recommendations and performs numerous actions by using the internet. Siri's American voice is said to be Susan Bennett done in July 2005. Karen Jacobsen is the Australian voice and Jon Briggs is the original British male voice.

Siri can make calls or send texts, read messages, give game scores, relate weather conditions, schedule events and give reminders, give travel instructions, turn on home devices and play music among many increasing uses. She can be recruited by simply calling out: Hey Siri. In 2015 this was upgraded for individualized voice recognition to lessen non-owner activation.

Sophia[33], a life-size female robot (humanoid or gynoid), from Hanson Robotics in Hong Kong, spoke at the United Nations in 2017 with UN Deputy Secretary-General Amina J. Mohammed, and appeared on the Jimmy Fallon show[34]. She has 62 appropriate facial expressions and voice recognition, built by Alphabet, Inc.

Her intelligence software was designed by SingulairtyNET. She can interact within narrow ranges and actually seems to carry on a conversation. It seems real because a camera in each eye makes eye contact. Some pre-written responses make it seem as if she is spontaneously interacting. Algorithms determine her reactions. She can process spoken and visual data. When Fallon asked her if she knew where she was, she answered "New York City" and "on my favorite TV show". That was probably pre-written. She can tell jokes and has reasonable timing. She can also be befriended on FaceBook. She has seven siblings, one (Bina48) passed a Notre Dame college course on philosophy on love. Experts seemed to think there's some fraud and deception. She's just a nice looking chatbox, designed only to handle a few very limited situations. Yann LeCun, a well known computer scientist, said: "Sophia's skills are complete bullshit." Experts warn us to watch out for the ELIZA effect which is the tendency to unconsciously assume computer behaviors are analogous to human behaviors.

Innovative groups in the near future will be able to create any voice you want to talk and/or entertain you, keep you company or lull you to sleep. Pick your celebrity and simply put in a request(s). You might be able to select a voice among many like picking a radio station. There can be many abuses. Imagine getting a phony, urgent phone call from a child or from your what seems like your spouse

---

33 Taylor, Harriet "Could You Fall in Love with Robot Sophie. "Could you fall in love with robot Sophia?". *CNBC.* (March)3, 2016).

34 Taylor, Harriet, "Meet Sophia, the Female Humanoid Robot and Newest SXSW Celebrity."*PCWorld* .(March 03, 2016)

asking the numbers on a credit card. One can already listen to a Trump or Obama simulation on Montreal's Lyrebird website. The science isn't quite there, but it's getting close. Imagine a court hearing a capital crime case in the future with a conviction that features a computer-simulated, fake confession.

Did Evolution Play A Role?

Sending and receiving messages is critical to survival for all living beings on this planet, whether that be simple touch, chemicals, visual cues, electric pulses, body sounds, body language, gestures or complex speech.

There is evidence that making sound could have begun way back with some of the first forms of life. If this is proof of evolution, one needs to explain the enormity and complexity of each individual step.

Microorganisms use chemicals to communicate. The bacteria Vibrio fischeri will suddenly glow when a colony reaches critical concentration. It's called quorum sensing. Fire flies, bats and bees do this, too. One might liken this troop leader barking out an order. Or, a team captain waiting for all the team members to arrive. Something triggers the entire group when they are ready.

The bacteria pseudomonas and salmonella communicate in similar ways when causing diseases in people. It's as if these microscopic organisms can determine, in advance, or know through their genes the minimum number of bacteria needed to kill off their host. Once that number is reached or the stockpiles of toxins are enough, an order goes out to disseminate. These nearly invisible entities communicate by auto-inducers(chemicals) and "hear" by complimentary chemical receptors. How these messages can travel so quickly and which individuals(s) decides it's time to attack remains unclear. We can stop quorum sensing in some situations with quorum quenchers (other chemicals).

Insects also speak to one another. We know ants communicate by laying pheromones (hormones) down when trailblazing (like Hansel and Gretel leaving bread crumbs). Or, painting hormones on their exoskeleton, rubbing antennae, and issuing visual displays such as different dances. Pheromones are also used to identify nests and establish social orders.

Mature pupae, according to a study by Karsten Schönrogge, an entomologist at the Centre for Ecology & Hydrology, Wallingford, United Kingdom, showed, using an extra-sensitive microphone, that mature pupae and adult ants communicate by making brief sounds by scraping their hind legs against a specialized spike on their abdomen. The study showed that immature pupae and those who had this spike removed could not call for help. And, then there's the caterpillar from the Nessus sphinx hawk moth, per Jayne Yack of Carleton University in Ottawa. It will emit through its mouth, if disturbed, a hiss and a series of scratchy sounds. One can hear these sounds on You-Tube.

Dinosaurs probably produced and heard sounds. And just maybe, they were not as scary as made out in the movies. We don't know if they had some form of vocal cords as the required tissues are considered soft and cannot fossilize. Maybe they were bird-like, chirps on steroids. Most scientists believe they had inner ears that were similar to modern day birds. Given the presence of feathers, that makes some sense.

We also know fish make sounds. The ocean, experts say, is a noisy place with thousands of species making pops, clicks, whistles, purrs, grunts, barks, hums, hoots, rattles and tinkles. Their sounds (vibrations) are heard by specialized bones in their head called ear bones and lateral lines found along both sides of their bodies. **Noted Neo-Darwinists say these ear bones moved and connected with certain jaw bones to form our ears, but there are no in-between steps (fossils).** Textbooks often say fish have a narrower range of sounds and decibels than we have, but I always doubt conclusions. Experts have throughout history not known what they didn't know and drew unsatisfactory conclusions.

Lizards can hear, typically 500-4000Hz range. They have visible ear openings. Although many lizards communicate by push-ups, some actually "speak." Geckos are especially known for making sounds. Known as "the devil in the trees",the New Caledonia, at 14 inches in length, growls. Male tokay geckos have a mating call that sounds like tokay, tokay, which might be our misunderstanding and actually be today, today. The gila monster hisses. Their inner ear only has one bone—the stapes or stirrup. Not three, like we have. Snakes can hear low frequency sounds. They don't have ears, but they do have a single ear bone attached to their jaw. Our bones are not attached to jaw bones. Somehow in evolution theory they moved on their own accord. Interestingly, some people can hear, by conducting sounds from and through their jaw bones.

Mice can speak (and hear) at different wavelengths, some of which we cannot hear. It's not just the cartoonish squeak, but there are special sounds used while diddling in their nests and when frightened. Males use an ultrasound song to attract females (this one we cannot hear) and females have discussions with their female friends using ultrasound. Probably about who's hot and who's not.

Everyone knows birds communicate by singing, whistles, tweets, warbles, honks and many other ways. In the morning it might be males affirming their territories. Later, it might be seduction. The quality and depth of song repertoires suggest fitness. There are alarm calls telling others of a danger and mobbing calls that recruit help. Chickadees warn the entire neighborhood, there's danger approaching. The forest will automatically turn silent.

Birds have vocal cords that are anatomically different from ours, but found in a similar place. Their ears are inconspicuous openings behind each eye, usually protected by special feathers. These feathers blunt the affect of wind and/or pressures if the bird dives into water. The inner ear only has one bone (the columella), on contrast to the human ear which has three bones (stapes, malleolus and hammer).

Whales communicate and hear in ways that oftentimes exceed human capabilities. They use frequent, high-frequency clicks and echolocation to assess their environment and find food. The humpback whale has a distinct song. Dolphins's ears are tiny slits at the bottom of their heads. They can hear seven times better than we. They also have sonar called echolocation and can hear the shape, size, density and speed of the objects hundreds of yards away.

Even plants and trees communicate. Shortly after a giraffe starts grazing on Acacia, the tree releases ethylene to discourage the giraffe(s) and to notify their neighbors of the attack. A number of different plants release specific chemical signals to birds saying they need help with caterpillars. Tobacco, corn and cotton plants have volatile chemical SOS signals that summon predators like wasps.

Monkeys might have the right anatomy to speak as we do, according evolutionist Bill Tecumseh Sherman Fitch[35], but they don't the right wiring. He has studied sounds a macaque monkey under X-ray video. Other researchers have said their vocal cords don't close adequately to make our sounds; they would need a different kind of control of their tongue and lower jaw. That is, billions new and/or different neural connections in the brain.

Monkeys can definitely communicate with us, better than other animals. Washoe was the best known chimp to use American Sign Language (ASL). After six years of training, she could sign 150 words including play, food and tickling. The best known gorilla to use sign language was Koko, who, it was claimed, understood more than 1000 signs, called Gorilla Sign Language (GSL) by her trainer Francine

35 Fitch, W. T. (1997). "Vocal Tract Length and Formant Frequency Dispersion Correlate with Body Size in Rhesus Macaques." Journal of the Acoustical. Society of America 102: 1213-1222.
Fitch, W. T. (2000). "The Evolution of Speech: a Comparative Review," Trends Cog. Sci. 4, 258-267

Patterson. She also understood over 2000 spoken words. Koko even made up her own words such as finger bracelet for ring. The hearing mechanisms (ears) in monkeys and apes are very similar to ours, but they can hear much better.

But no animal can think in the abstract as we can, no matter how smart or so many think. And, this is not a subtle or small genetic change.

Parrots can imitate a variety of words and sounds from different languages including swear words and a toilet flushing. One parrot returned to its home in England after four years away, swearing in Spanish. An African Grey parrot named Alex had a vocabulary of 100 words, but there are serious questions about any comprehension. Inflection, loudness, and circumstances impact understanding. This is particularly true when communicating with dogs and cats.

Dolphins have unique ways of communicating. To make "vocal" sounds they blow inhaled air through the blowholes and past "monkey lips" that vibrate accordingly. These vibrations are sent to a fatty "melon" in the head where the vibrations are converted to sound. They can also whistle, click and buzz. We cannot hear most of the clicks, which have a frequency around 100 kHz. Note sound waves underwater move at an unbelievable 3355 mph whereas sound outside water moves at 768 mph. Nature seems to have known that with this design. Our ears cannot pinpoint the source of an underwater sound. We hear lower kHZ.

Dolphins are over one hundred times faster than humans at processing sound. We can distinguish two clicks that arrive 30-50 milliseconds max. Dolphins can do the same at 264 microseconds. The auditory pathways in dolphin brains are large and there's reason to believe they can create mental images with their clicks. Blind folks have been known to do this. Blind Ben is one of the better known. He was blinded by cancer in both eyes at age two. He learned to use clicks on his own and much like bats and dolphins he can "see" his world. He's able to shoot hoops with a basketball, ride a bike and work through any number of obstacle courses.

Human Hearing

Without the ability to hear and communicate, prehistoric man probably would not have survived very long—if at all. Other senses might have stepped up somehow, but it's unlikely they would ever be enough. At a minimum, the earliest hunters and warriors would have needed to hear danger, look for some confirmation and possibly warn others (who must also be able hear). Sign language, facial expressions and/or lip reading could have played some role, but it would have been minuscule. How does a "cave" mother care for her newborn if she cannot hear? It seems as though crying and hearing had to have come together., very early on.

Note that hearing and speech are very complicated systems that involve hundreds to tens of thousands of interacting, successive steps working in parallel and simultaneous ways. They have to match up just as birds recognize other birds and dolphins speak to the dolphins. This is so much more than simply having the right receiver and speaker.

Add in a pair of lungs to inhale air through a moist opening(a nose preferably), lungs to exhale the air, vocal cords that can stretch and contract in near infinite ways, diaphragms to control specific volumes of air, rib connections that can expand and contract, cilia to keep lung passages clean, nerves to control diaphragm movement, a mouth and lips to form specific sounds(words), face muscles to work the jaws, an area of the brain to control every syllable, other areas of the brain to understand the meaning of incoming sounds/signals and an area(s) of the brain to issue appropriate responses. There are scores of controlling muscles and nerves involved in any action. Every one of these can be construed as a step in an unparalleled stairwell. And, this is a simplified overview.

Evolution theory states our larynx descended over time so that we could speak. What a convenient accident(that worked out perfectly)? We hear a specific range of sounds, which includes all vocals other humans make. A lucky coincidence? Frogs and bats hear a range that is appropriate for them. Unless we're seated in a sound-proof room, we usually cannot hear our heart beat, lungs breathing, throat swallowing saliva, stomach sloshing and gurgling, intestines moving their excretory packets, ureters dripping urine into the bladder and any close-by arterial blood humming. That's a good thing; a design thing, I believe. Or, else we'd be badly distracted and possibly go mad.

As odd as earlobes may appear, they are specifically designed to magnify pitch as well as collect and funnel sounds into the ear canals where they bounce around by the tens of thousands(+). The earlobes are strategically placed on both sides of our head to determine distance, movement and direction of sound. Never found at the top of the head, inside the armpits or the back of the thighs. Those sound waves bounce against the eardrum (tympanic membrane) which is a semi-clear membrane, resembling tight Saran wrap®. It is exquisitely sensitive and vibrates with the different sound waves. It's quite interesting how it handles so many different sounds coming in at the same time.

Butting up against the inside of the eardrums are three bones(the hammer, anvil and the stirrup). They carry virtually all messages to the inner ear which is a snail shell-shape organ, filled with fluid and about 25000 hair fibers. The vibrations are capture by these hairs, as if individual ones were assigned to collect a different sound wave. These messages are collected and sent, via the auditory nerve, to the brain for translation and possible action. The receiving parts of the brain are called the temporal lobes of which there are two. Within nanoseconds the right and left lobes of the brain coordinate what is being heard. And, through no conscious effort, hear the whole orchestra. Or, you can selectively hear the French horns or the violins. A symphony is an auditory movie.

We can communicate with the outside world by talking, whispering, singing, writing, drawing, mimicking, whistling, blinking, typing, touching and signing. Many people who are deaf can still communicate, unless the disability arose with a certain stroke or direct injury. If the expressive areas of the brain are damaged, virtually all means of connecting with the world are sadly blocked. It's my experience from talking to stroke victims who have had the crisis reversed early on, they knew what they want to say, but the wrong words, if any words, come out, instead. One patient of mine of mine would answer "Yeah right" to any question and I couldn't help believing he understand. He'd get visibly upset slamming his fist down sometimes, but his only words were "Yeah right."

Scientists don't know the origin of speech. It cannot be measured and, of course, there were no prehistoric recording devices. Theories abound that include grunts changing into meaningful grunts, shrieks into calls for help, cries into meaningful complaints and surprises into laughter. Babies must have always cried to let parents know something was needed (like food). Somewhere along the way, hunters had to have meaningful communications during hunts for food.

We each have a vocabulary of 25,000 words(on ave.). Considering pitch, volume, gestures, intonations and body language, we have a near-infinite number of ways to make our thoughts known. Multiply that by approximately 180 languages. Could that be accidental or coincidental?

...the longer you look, the more you realize that we have built human-like machines for a very long time: robots have played a key role in helping us establish our sense of ourselves and of our place in the wider world.

ROBOTS: THE 500-YEAR QUEST TO MAKE MACHINES HUMAN, BEN RUSSELL, EDITOR

VIII
The Smell And Taste Piece

In contrast to certain senses that can be augmented by devices such as the magnifying glass or by cupping one's hand, the need to taste food has, in certain circumstances, fallen on other people. In the case of food, servants who do this are called food tasters and for liquids they are called cupbearers. In ancient Rome, many of these lucky folks were slaves, termed praegustators. Slaves probably prayed that their masters were well liked before checking the evening meal. The employers were typically the richest and extremely powerful. If the taster became severely ill or succumbed later that day, his or her job was considered well done. Perhaps, given a pat of gratitude on the back just before dying.

Adolf Hitler had a food taster who tasted his food every morning at 8:00AM. President Putin has a food taster as part of his security staff and President Obama never traveled (and ate) without his taster along. Meetings were altered if the taster couldn't make it. One such incident is documented.

A fully functional humanoid will need some sense of smell and/or taste. They won't be eating or drinking, of course, short of feigning it, but they may be used to chemically verify the quality of food. No doubt versions of a tasting robot will be also found at many agriculture plants, grocery outlets, restaurants and a few homes.

The E-tongue or gustatory analytic device which doesn't look anything like a tongue, is an instrument that measures and compares tastes; it can detect "flavors" at lower concentrations (thresholds) than we can. It can quantify saltiness and distinguish poisons. Might one, when trying a new restaurant, pull out a mechanical tongue to taste one's meal first?

The first tasting device was invented by Professor Fredrik Winquist of Linköping University, Sweden, who had significant input in electronic noses, also. These machines can detect dissolved compounds much like a human tongue does and forward electronic messages. Presently, these machines are being used for analyzing flavor in aging beverages, and helping to find ways to mask the tastes of medicines. The latter is for children who won't take capsules that can obscure chemical tastes.

Mechanical noses may not be needed to detect kitty litter odor, warn another about the need to use deodorant or decide the quality of a fragrance, but they may achieve skills that exceed a canine's ability to detect explosives and narcotics. They should be able help find cadavers. Along with dogs, they may be patrolling among airports, bus stations, sports arenas, train stations and political marches.

The use of electronic noses somewhat overlaps electronic tongues. Work in this area began around 1982 and has rapidly improved. Industry uses these mechanisms to assess the pleasantness (or unpleasantness) of flavors and scents. They are also used for the detection of spoilage, contamination and batch consistency.

Electronic "tongues" and "noses" are not used by restaurants yet, but future menus might include a series of robotic quality tests. There might be a grade for how spicy and how salty? Might a General or an Admiral, during wartime, be worried about his/her food? Note some poisons take hours to work, easily passing by a living tester/

taste whereas the machine might catch those immediately. And, live to test another day.

Human Smell And Taste

Most people think that taste occurs in the mouth. It certainly seems so. By design, perhaps, we have to be fooled. Food, for obvious reasons, needs to go through the mouth and not through the nose, but taste has to reside very close by. We might think that a five-course meal tasted great, but that partly means most of the dinner smelled great. The tongue is limited. It picks up salty, sweet, bitter, sweet and umami(broth, savory, certain meat taste). The remaining millions(+) tastes are located in the nose; they combine in ways like a symphony. There may be violins, then piano, then both. Everything we eat or drink has a unique chemical signature. Every combination has another taste. The possibilities are astronomical.

Qualia plays a role here as well. This is not a word we commonly use, but it's the subjective quality of something we sense that cannot be explained. To recognize how difficult this process is pretend that you want to describe the taste of an orange to an extra-terrestrial; you cannot use any comparisons. Just try describing the color turquoise without making comparisons. Tell someone what Middle C sounds like without comparisons or graphs of sound waves.

E-olfactory machines have been improving. They will soon be able to detect the thousands of odors and flavors that we can detect plus several dangerous scents we cannot. Not only identify, but compare and quantify each. No human can detect levels of carbon monoxide or radon gas, but your private robot may eventually alert you. In industry they are used for quality control watching for conformity, managing raw material variability and comparison of the effects of manufacturing processes on products.

Future applications include detection of harmful bacteria in wounds and hospital ventilation systems, and the detection of volatile substances manufactured by different malignancies like lung cancer.

Tongue Piece

The tongue not only contributes to select components of taste, but it is critical to swallowing and speech. Every tongue has a "tongue print" that can be used by security devices for identifications along with iris scanners and facial recognition.

The average length of a tongue is 10 cm or 4.5 inches, males slightly longer than females; there are individuals that can touch both earlobes and the tip of their nose. The tongue has incredibly complex, muscle control, is exquisitely sensitive to irritating and painful stimuli, can readily sense hot and cold, repairs itself better than any other tissue, and simply settles into the shallow of the lower mouth when not needed. It automatically moves food around the mouth for processing and throws it to the back for swallowing. It's the only muscle that doesn't work with the skeletal system (a bone or joint). If it were split in half lengthwise, the two halves can act like separate tongues. They can actually and weirdly cross over like crossed fingers.

The tongue's surface has approximately 3000 taste buds. Most taste buds are found toward the back of tongue, but in babies there's many more, some in the roof of the mouth, down the throat, and along the cheeks. A large part of the baby's life is eating (and tasting). In addition to the five traditional types of taste receptors, there are some that pick up carbonation and fattiness. Molecules that give food a pleasant taste are described as sapid. Other sensors include the vanilloid receptors that detect "heat" from molecules like capsaicin, CMR1 receptors for "cold" from menthol, trigeminal for actual heat and cold and several that have to do with mechanical characteristics such as loose, dry, lumpy, crunchy and smooth. Other contenders for taste, called putative, are soapiness, lysine, electric, alkaline, hydroxide and metallic.

Three nerves innervate the tongue: vagus, glossopharyngeal and facial. The taste buds and sensors in the nasal olfactory areas convert chemicals(tastes) into a host of different nerve signals that travel back to a large sensory area of the brain. This area is larger than an arm or leg area in the human brain. To test this, have someone peel an orange next to you and see if you don't taste it. Note wine experts taste wines by swirling a partially full glass and then taking a few quick sniffs at the rim. By stepping away to allow the taste to filter through the nose, they get the best taste. That's without swallowing.

Twenty-five percent of people are super-tasters, somewhat like folks with greater than 20:20 vision, better than normal hearing or faster reflexes. They have a heightened sense of taste, especially when it comes down to bitter foods.

Like hearing and vision, the different tastes from a large meal can be a symphony of sensations. Certain "instruments" may play a solo.

Robot Smell Piece

Mechanical smell overlaps mechanical taste. They may not even be housed in exactly the same places as a human being. Might a robot taste with its fingertips—like a fly that tastes with its feet? There's no tongue. Might a robot detect smoke through its ears or a portal in a hand? There's no rule for these decisions. In fact, a robot might hear through a receiver on its chest.

The smoke detector fire alarm was invented by Francis Robbins Upton in 1890. Carbon monoxide and even carbon dioxide detection came about during the late twentieth century. Any can easily be added to robots. Geiger counters have been used since the 1950s during the cold war when a nuclear attack was imminent. Nowadays they are maintained by fire and emergency services besides the military. NASA routinely checks returning flights from outer space for radioactive debris. Nuclear storage sites check for leaks routinely.

Machines can sense radiation using Geiger counters and the day may come they will be standard issue in androids. These instruments can detect ionizing radiation This protection is needed in academic institutions, certain research centers, large medical facilities and certain military centers. Geigers detect alpha beta particles, beta particles and gamma rays.

Smoke detectors have become or should become standard equipment in homes, office buildings and industries. Our lives depend on these machines as they will sense a dangerous presence long before we might. Nearly two-thirds of death from house fires happen in homes without smoke detectors. Especially as we sleep. Robots used by emergency services will need to be outfitted with smoke detectors. Your android will be outfitted with a host of emergency devices and a smoke detector will likely be one of them.

Human Smell Piece

The sense of smell, aka olfaction, is present for the detection of hazards, recognizing pheromones(sex hormone signals), identifying MHC genes(to prevent incest) and picking up trillions of subtle components of taste. The olfactory bulb, the receiving unit, is located high inside each nostril. It traps odorants (the components of scents). Think of them as an uncountable number of convoluted, complex, different-colored keys matching up exactly with uncountable, matching locks. Once the signals are initiated they are modified by glomerulus and sent to the brain along the olfactory nerve. All this happens in milliseconds and can move along like a movie scene.

Of interest: the sensing areas of a human nose totals about 1.6 sq. in. whereas the dog has 26 sq. in. Plus the dog has hundred times the number of receptors per any area measured. We can detect blood relatives by their scent. Theory says this prevents animals from engaging in sexual acts with close family members. A similar mechanism, called the Westermarck effect, applies to the desensitization of sexual attraction to biological partners after a few years of living together. Mothers can identify by body odor their biological children, but not their stepchildren.

Olfaction is also deeply involved in romance. Animals seem to innately know this. We don't give it much thought, except whenever perfumes and colognes are around.

In addition to sex pheromones there are alarm-pheromones, food trail pheromones used by social insects, territorial pheromones found in urine of felines and canines, and hive attractant pheromones used by bees. Mice and other animals seem to use pheromones to avoid inbreeding. Animals commonly secrete these when it's time for breeding. We apparently don't. We wear bikinis and tight clothes.

The vomeronasal organ or Jacobson's organ is the part of the nose that is responsible for reception of pheromones (sex-attractant) hormones. It is found at the base of our nasal septum when we are born and slowly shrinks after that. Although it can even disappear from sight, its presence is always felt. We are pleasantly compelled to love others who match up. With advanced age, we either lose the ability to detect pheromones or we are less impacted by the presence. Or, perhaps, both. Wives can identify their husband's sweaty tee shirts from a batch of other men. Mothers and daughters will often have periods simultaneously and young women in sorority dorms have time-coordinated periods. This is all hormone mediated, not group-think.

This organ detects sex hormones that all animals secrete, species specific, to attract a lover. It can impact social behavior in many ways and can be found in unicellular life, multicellular life, plants, insects and all vertebrates. In essence we "lap up" by kissing and/or breathing in this mind-altering chemical when romancing. Noted, only teenagers can kiss for hours, magnetized by pheromones.

"The only thing worse than being blind is having sight, but no vision."

HELEN KELLER, FAMOUS AUTHOR, LECTURER, WHO LOST HER SIGHT AND HEARING AT AGE 19 MONTHS DUE TO SCARLET FEVER. SHE LEARNED TO COMMUNICATE BY TOUCH.

IX
The Touch Piece

Humanoids will surely need to have a sense of touch which includes vibration, pressure, temperature, and pain which, for them, means destructive forces like excessive heat and corrosive chemicals.

Having a robot paramedic suture a wound or assist in eye surgery requires "fingers" that have a very sophisticated sense of touch. Lifting children requires different pressure than lifting boxes. Dismantling a bomb requires another kind of touch. Breaking open an egg is a lot different from breaking open a coconut. For good measure, it might help if the "skin" of certain humanoids, especially those that work closely with people, actually had the feel of real skin with a thermostat set at 98.6°. Android nurses with ice-cold hands may be disliked.

It's not easy to find the date(s) when mankind tried to duplicate the sense of touch. Certainly, cavemen used sticks to prod animals along. Sometime during the early Renaissance Period, an unnamed someone noticed that water, alcohol and, later on, mercury would expand and shrink with temperature changes. Santorio Santorio, a Venetian physician-inventor, and Galileo Galilei, an Italian inventor, at the turn of the sixteenth century, are both given credit for inventing the thermoscope. This invention made use of the fact that water expands with heat,

In 1724, Gabriel Fahrenheit, a Dutch physicist, invented the mercury-in-glass thermometer. He placed a thermometer-like device in a bath of ice, water and ammonium chloride and marked that finding 0°. Then he used water on the edge of freezing(slight ice) and assigned it 32° and then, he marked boiling water at 212° by comparing it to mercury. He then determined that a person's temperature was 96° which actually was close, but not quite right.

Although the measurement of water's freezing point of 32°F and boiling of 212°F were first used, some scientists have shifted to using centigrade or Celsius. This was named after a Swedish inventor who, in 1742, devised a more logical scale with freezing marked at 0°C and boiling 100° Celsius.

Anton de Haen, an Austrian-Dutch medical student of Hermann Boerhaave, during the mid 1700s, is thought to be responsible for adding thermometers to medical assessment of patients to document fever. He carried a thermometer to every bedside. It wasn't until 1868, however that Carl Wunderlich helped define the normal range of temperature for humans.

For decades 98.6° has been considered normal even though patients would later argue that they normally run high or low. We now know, with a few exceptions, that anything between 97°F and 100.4°F can be normal. A fever for one person could even be 98.6. We now have very accurate oral, rectal and axillary mercury thermometers. The rectal option is considered the most accurate (and least desired). Other versions include electronic ear thermometers, thermometers that can be wiped against or held against the forehead, plastic strips that change color when tightly pressed against skin, and thermometers hidden inside pacifiers.

Infrared and laser thermometers are the newest innovations; they are commonly used for monitoring equipment in industry. It's likely that robots will be using some variation of this as shoving a robotic finger into a throat or elsewhere will not be well received. Versions are already used in hospitals to measure patient temperatures without touching them (very important with contagious diseases like Ebola), checking for hot spots when fire fighting and checking for mechanical problems(overheating).

A flexible electronic skin (e-skin) that looks like our skin has not been invented, but work toward that end is well on its way. In 2009, Ted Adelson's research group at MIT announced a sensor technology called Gelsight that could discern hardness and 3-D map a surface beneath a robot finger. In 2010, scientists at Stanford University and the University of California, Berkeley developed a gentle, electronic skin that can feel touch. Its sensors can monitor both vital signs and brain waves. In 2011, Stanford researchers developed a stretchable solar cell for skin usage and in 2012 they came up with self-healing, plastic and nickel skin.

In 2013 the University of Cincinnati developed the first e-skin that could actually sweat. It turns out we secrete minute amounts of sweat in our hands to improve grip. In 2016, Cornell University announced they had developed a fabricated hand, attached to a robotic arm, that can feel its surroundings. Stretchable optical wave-guides have been around for 50 years, but Professor Robert Shepherd with The Organic Robotics Lab has been able to couple them with soft lithography plus 3-D printing. Pressure is "sensed" by how much light is lost to a photodiode when the finger(s) bend. His group's project was able to "feel" three tomatoes and actually tell which was the ripest.

In 2017 a team from Caltech and ETH Zurich announced the development of an artificial skin that can detect temperature changes. It can be used by amputees in prosthetic limbs and on top of skin injuries to monitor for temperature changes (infection). The "skin" uses a technology learned from a pit viper to sense prey.

A report in the Journal of Science Advances, 2018, described a thin, yellow, adhesive sticker that can monitor pressure, temperature, humidity and air flow. It can stretch, bend and even be recycled (re-heal). According to the main author Jianliang Xiao[36] a robot can simply touch an ill child and immediately know its temperature. Further work resulted in degrees of pressure demonstrated by the intensity of a yellow luminescence.

So far most electronic skin perception is dependent upon on more central sensors like vision. A strong contender for future technology is work done at Harvard on soft robot grippers that can sense movement, pressure, touch and temperature. At UCLA and the University of Washington work proceeds on stretchable artificial skin that feel vibrations.

A hand should be able to move and feel at the same time. Optics in spongey fingers can tell texture. We can tell a fork from a spoon by shape if hidden from view. But reaching into a dark hole and sensing anything more than it's not a porcupine, without visual assistance is still down the road for robots. That said a warm, friendly handshake may be here momentarily.

The question comes up: Should the surface of a humanoid have a realistic appearance? And, then which race? Or, would a chameleon-capability be in order, depending on the dominant race of the surrounding community? Octopuses and cuttle fishes can hide in any environment. The technology must be out there. Changing skin color might be most helpful for those professions that require travel in hostile environments. Perhaps, add a sprinkling of freckles, even a scar or mole. Hard like a sheet of metal won't cut it. Skin must be soft. Should extra energy be put into keeping the skin feeling warm, perhaps, 98.6° F, to others? Otherwise, someone might be able to tell they are fake people just by the touch. Nothing worse than having a cold robot caress you in the morning.

36 Zhanan Zou1,*, Chengpu Zhu2,*, Yan Li1, Xingfeng Lei2,3, Wei Zhang2,† and Jianliang Xiao1,†Science Advances 09 Feb 2018:Vol. 4, no. 2, eaaq0508DOI: 10.1126/sciadv.aaq0508

Post-doctoral, robotic fellow Akihiko Yamaguchi has developed finger-vision using a miniature camera watching black dots shift on a cellophane sheet. Without slippage, it can peel bananas which is a very difficult task for robots. Cornell has developed a robot hand that can actually feel tomatoes and determine which is the ripest by internal LED sources and changes in wavelengths with compression.

The Evolution Piece

The theory of evolution doesn't tell us when the sense of touch arrived. Common sense, using their scheme, would suggest it had to be very early on. The first organisms tumbled about, moved about by the whims of wind and water, good and bad luck. At some point these organisms had to take some control over their immediate destiny. New blueprints would be needed, new ways to assess their neighborhood, yet biologists have not found a way that any living entity can add brand new DNA (instructions). Mutations or accidents would have made things worse. Natural selection may have favored those who could sense even a little, but where did that skill come from? A single, beneficial mutation would not likely be enough.

Virtually all living beings have some version of touch, including the common cold virus. These minuscule entities may or may not qualify as life forms, but they definitely display design and purpose. Every virus seems to have proteins on its surface that are used to penetrate the surface of a sinus, nasal and/or throat cell. The polio virus enters through mouth, from fecal contamination, and eventually penetrates nerve cells. The herpes virus enters through lip, mouth, genitals or anus. They seem to know exactly where to go and what to do although just their huge numbers help accidental contact. One might ask how these road maps came about. By mistake?

Bacteria like the ones that cause strep throat or dysentery, are much larger, living organisms (yet microscopic) and they, too, have a specific way of finding their target(s). These "germs" are said to lack sensory organs and cannot feel pain. Yet, there's some evidence that they can perceive their environment. Select microorganisms tend to migrate to areas that are warm or cold, areas of light or dark, areas of normal oxygen or ones with low oxygen, and/or toward areas with nutrients. Some move by flagella, which are rotary motors. Some actually swim. Amoebae throw a part of their body in the direction of their goal and pull the rest of the body along. This takes smarts. New smarts.

A 2017 study by Giancarlo N. Bruni[37] from UC Boulder showed that E. coli bacteria get excited when poked. They send out calcium ion signals which are a mechanism that is similar to vertebrate sensory nervous systems. We know salmonella, whose family can cause typhoid fever, become more efficient at infecting when placed on a stiff surface rather than a soft one. Why remains a mystery.

A study by Isabelle Hug[38] strongly suggests the bacteria Caulobacter can feel. This organism has a propeller (flagellum) that moves it toward target food or cell. When it comes up against a cell wall, it immediately secretes an adhesive substance. The tail stops rotating (proton influx stops) and falls off.

Do plants feel? Scientists say no, because they lack a nervous system and brain, but that somewhat depends on how strictly one defines the sense of touch. Researchers in Australia[39] say plants can

---

37 Giancarlo N. Bruni, R. Andrew Weekley, Benjamin J. T. Dodd, and Joel M. Kralj "Voltage-gated Calcium Flux Mediates Escherichia coli Mechanosensation "www. pnas.org/content/114/35/9445.full or https://f1000.com/prime/728648738

38 PNAS, August 29, 2017. 114 (35) 9445-9450; published ahead of print August 14, 2017. https://doi.org/10.1073/pnas.1703084114

Edited by Richard Losick, Harvard University, Cambridge, MA, and approved July 21, 2017 (received for review February 27, 2017)

"Second Messenger–mediated Tactile Response by a Bacterial Rotary Motor" Isabelle Hug1, Siddharth Deshpande2,*, Kathrin S. Sprecher1, Thomas Pfohl2,†, Urs Jenall,‡*Science* 27 Oct 2017:Vol. 358, Issue 6362, pp. 531-534 DOI: 10.1126/science. aan5353

39 Olivier Van Aken (+61 8) 6488 2112 / (+61 4) 34 942 389 (ARC Centre of Excellence in Plant Energy Biology at UWA) David Stacey (UWA Media and Public Relations Manager) (+61 8) 6488 3229 / (+61 4) 32 637 716

feel and react to water droplets. Also, that the simple patting of leaves can change gene expression and metabolism. Two proteins, AtWRKY15 and AtWRKY40 are responsible.

We all know that carnivorous plants like the Venus flytrap and the pitcher plant can sense the presence of an insect (a meal) on their leaves. The venues fly trap plant closes its teeth-like leaves, trapping the visitor for days and digests it.

We know nature is loaded with plants and trees that send out alarm chemicals when they sense they are under attack. Is this caused by pain? Or, the sensation of touch? Or a chemical sense? No one knows for sure, but there's a study that suggests plants can cry for help[40]. They send a message to their roots, when under attack. The roots will then secret an acid that brings beneficial bacteria to the rescue. "Plants are a lot smarter than we give them credit for," said Harsh Bais, assistant professor of plant and soil sciences at the University of Delaware.

Insects can feel vibrations and mechanical disturbances. Most have tiny, sensory hairs (sensilla) found at the end of nerve cells; these react when touched. Try catching a fly. They can feel air moving as your hands approach. We know for certain moth larvae will roll over if touched with a hot pin. Who wouldn't? Yet, The consensus at this moment is that they don't feel pain. I'm not sure why.

Of interest on this topic is the famous essay, <u>Consider the Lobster</u>, by David Foster Wallace[41]. He says the lobster has internal nociceptors(pain sensors) that detect significant temperature changes in water and that they surely feel the boiling water when

40 "Plants Cry For Help," Live Science
https://www.livescience.com/2972-plants-cry.html
41 Wallace, David F. "Consider the Lobster." *Consider the Lobster: And Other Essays*. New York: Little, Brown, 2005. Print. 235-254.

cooked. He says their "struggling, thrashing, and lid clattering" demonstrates extreme fear and pain.

We know that some mollusks have the sense of touch. Octopuses have a fine sense of touch with their suction cups, often reaching, where it cannot see, into crevices for food. They do not withdraw if pinched by a crab's claw, but continue to attack. We don't know if they are simple stoics, have a high pain threshold or simply don't feel pain. There are some ethical dilemmas delivering pain to see if they can feel pain.

The Human Piece

Many, if not all, senses had to come about simultaneously, in the right places and be in sync. There's a limited benefit to touch without the help of sight. Seeing a container of water doesn't tell you how hot or cold it might be. Without pain sensation, one might miss the fact that a water-like fluid was actually very corrosive. Without pressure sensation, one wouldn't know their socks were cutting off circulation.

Life, without the sense of touch, would never have succeeded, certainly not as we know it. There has always been a need to touch, to familiarize oneself with one's surroundings.

There's also a strong need to know how intense a sensation is. Feeling the outside of a door (with the back of your hand) and finding it intolerably hot should warn you there's a fire on the other side and not to open it. The sun is out and it looks warm outdoors, but watch out, it actually might be freezing. It's important to distinguish a pin prick from a laceration. Are my shoelaces untied, is my belt too tight, are my socks slipping, or is my hat slipping are all silent until there's a problem?

Touch shows up very early for us. An unborn child responds to touch (and very likely to pain), as early as the first trimester of pregnancy. We know it will retract its feet with irritating (mild pain) stimuli at twenty weeks.

Touch helps us pick out healthy food, protect ourselves, and to show love to another. Helen Keller, who was deaf and blind, required touch for all communication. Touch moderates whether something is too hot to be handled. A nut must be grasped differently than an egg which is different from an apple. An uncooked egg feels differently than a hard-boiled egg. Touch tells us if the food is too squishy(spoiled?) or too hard (outdated?).

Our sensory system is constantly at work and on high alert. And, that's good thing. Every speck of one's body is silently and constantly touching (feeling) something. Take a moment and focus on any part of your body. Your knee is actually feeling a pant leg or a hem, your toes are resting against the tip of your shoes, and your shirt/blouse is touching your neck and shoulders. You may only notice your glasses if they start to fall off. For some parts it's just ambient air. Virtually all remain silent, unless you purposefully focus on that area. While you've been oblivious, your sensory system has not. It remains on guard.

Personal touch is vital for life. We know that from primate studies and some human studies. Newborns need to be touched, handled and loved by their parent(s)or substitutes on a frequent basis or else they may suffer emotional problems. Rarely, do people feel loved if there's no touching going on in a relationship.

Our skin is our largest organ. It keeps us at a comfortable temperature; blocks pathogens like bacteria and viruses, and helps regulate hydration. It can contract, stretch, and repair itself. Other than having different concentrations of pigments, we're virtually all the same. We bleed and bruise the same color; we also cry the same tears, which come in at least three chemical versions: one for happiness, sadness or daily lubrication. Note tears are clear on purpose.

We all probably experience our environment the same, too. Nerves cover our entire surface, like a very fine, invisible fishing net, going inside every crease. In some ways this net is more like an electrical field. If something penetrates the field, alarms go off. Any movement of body hair is sensed by root hair plexuses below the skin's surface.

Some of the most sensitive receptors can be found in our fingertips, toe tips, lips, genitals and anus. Note how the blind read Braille. I find that skill remarkable. The areas that are the most sensitive are logically the areas that should be. That is mostly for survival, but partly for pleasure.

The different nerve endings have easily identifiable, microscopic tips or endings. There's a frayed-wire look for pain and temperature, a flattened-football end for deep pressure, a leaf on a stem for pressure and a tiny flattened disc for light touch. Like drinking from a firehose the brain receives enormous amounts of information and then sorts it for translation and possible action. Far beyond 99.99999%, input results in no action.

Information is carried to the brain by three connecting, sequential nerves (wires). The first goes from the skin surface to the spinal cord. **The second goes up the spine, typically crossing to the other side. Evolutionists cannot explain why or how half the spinal cord switches sides. It looks braided. Millions of these wires change over.** The third segments go to the sensory areas in the opposite side of brain. Right hand pain goes to the left brain. Foot pain goes to a different area of the brain than a toothache. Left toe pain goes to the right brain. If you're right handed, it's the left side of the brain that controls this (is dominate). **There's no known explanation for this. It couldn't have happened by chance or accident. No evolutionary benefit and not a mutation.**

Human touch is coded differently depending on the intended message or how it might be viewed. For example, note how it might feel if someone you didn't like tried to hold your hand versus the touch of a loved partner. Technically, the skin to skin feeling is the same and the squeeze may have same strength, but the sensations are received quite differently. Compare the touch of lover to an erotic area versus a complimentary pat on the shoulder. Brain scans using a functional MRI can reflect the different subjective feelings (i.e., degrees of pleasantness).

There can be a rainbow of sensations. Skin receptors (exteroceptors) can also tell if a surface is smooth, rough, hard, bumpy, scaly, fragile, crusty, soft, sharp, loaded with splinters, has thorns and/or dangerous. Certain sense receptors (called proprioceptors) found in muscles, tendons and joints also tell us about pain, position, swelling, tightness, movement, degrees of flexion and degrees of extension. Your feet (among other systems) tell you whether you are stable, vertical and what kind of surface you are walking on. Visceral sensors (interoceptors) tell us about inner goings-on such as feeling hungry, full, thirsty, if your blood pressure is too high (e.g. headache), if you're not getting enough oxygen (shortness of breath) and if you are suffering a heart attack (chest pain).

Temperature sensing is called thermo-reception and these cells, like many, are on duty 24/7. Based on those measurements, the body will adjust sweating and surface blood flow, whether we need to put on extra clothing or less, and whether we need extra fluids.

Noted we all have millions, if not billions, of internal sensors. They relay such things as the pain from appendicitis to shortness of breath to an ankle sprain. They tell us if our knee(s) or arm(s) are flexed, literally the position of every joint and any changes in real time. Discriminative-touch gives us the daily information like type of contact(s), location, movement, range, and intensity and any combinations. Haptic perception tells us what we are feeling. Close your eyes and see if you can tell the difference between a bobby pin, a diaper pin and a clothes pin. No question, you can. There's an emotional-touch which can distinguish a partner's loving touch. As we age, we slowly lose touch receptors. Our feet might not feel the ground as well and some of us endure falls. Note seeing particles of food on the face of old people. They cannot tell it's there.

I would guess, you get the message. We are a constant feeling machine. A machine that sends an enormous amount of information to our biological computer through an inexplicable circuitous route. Note many different symphonies are arriving from other senses such as vision, hearing and smell at the same time.

There is an unfortunate medical condition wherein people cannot feel pain, anywhere, in any form. They have to be extremely cautious their entire life. They are called touch blind. Our species would never have survived if we started off so impaired.

Other Senses Also Needed By A Humanoid

Balance monitoring resides in both inner ears next to the hearing apparatuses. Basically it senses body movement and is complemented by the senses of position or proprioception (meaning everything skin, bones, and joints) and vision. Without it we could never stand motionless (let alone stand up), walk, run, jump, bend over or handle a carnival ride. Without it we could never have hunted or fished for food or procreated. These two systems consist of three structures: cochlea, vestibule, and three semicircular canals.

These tubular canals lie in three planes and act like a gyroscope filled with fluid. As we shift body location this fluid go in different ways moving hairlike structures, which, in turn, stimulates the vestibular nerve. Motion is converted to electrical signals that are sent to the cerebellum. Here, the information is integrated with all information from the skeletal system from our toes to our head, everything skin involved and vision. This is a massive job that is accomplished on a nanosecond by nanosecond basis.

And, there's the proprioception sense that has to do with position sense. For example, do you know where your hands are? Your feet are? Your body in relation to the room? Walk across a room and this sense tells you where every part of your body is located, compared to the walls, chairs, tables and lights (without any thought of yours). This sense involves virtually every part of the brain.

Interoception or the internal sense gives you information from inside the body. This sense tells you if you have heartburn or rib pain. If you are hungry or full (energy homeostasis). If you are behind in fluids(thirsty). If you are short of breath, it tells you to breathe more deeply or quickly. If your knee is inflamed from arthritis, it tells you to stay off it. If you're having a heart attack, it tells you there's pain in your chest. If you are sick to your stomach and need to vomit. If you are cold, hot, overheated, fearful, stressed, distended from gas or constipation (stretch receptors), need to urinate, swallowed something too large(stretch receptors) or bitter/toxic.

Humanoids, of course will be different. No need to know if there's a stroke or gut problems, but they will need to monitor charge and all functions.

Chronoception refers to how the passage of time is perceived. The suprachiasmatic nucleus is responsible for the circadian (or daily) rhythm. Other cell clusters appear to be capable of timekeeping. No question humanoids will need to keep track of time.

"The reason the major blood vessels are along the inside of arms and the legs is because this was designed to protect them from the bite of a saber-toothed tiger."

A PARAMEDIC SAYING

X

Upper And Lower Extremities Piece

Robot Locomotion Piece

Should humanoids walk and move about exactly as people do? The likely answer is a probable yes. Four legs or even six might function better, especially when it comes to balance, carrying heavy loads, and speed, but would people feel comfortable with a part humanoid, part arachnoid waiter. Yet, multiple extremities might expedite housework.

Developing humanlike walking requires complex mathematics and engineering. Problems include a need to keep both legs moving at the same , and sometimes variable, speed, firm planting of each foot, proper shifting of weight, constant attention to torque, stride height and length, appropriate center of balance changes with speed and direction, and keeping the upper(heavier) torso in balance. Note: if you make a stack of books with the heavier and wider books on the tops, it will always fall over. So, might a robot without planning.

An ambulatory robot also has to be attentive to the type of terrain, traps like holes and all obstacles. There might be a wall or fence, a fallen tree or a large branch, a giant mud puddle, a sudden wind gust, a horn honking, or someone shouting there's a danger.

Humans do much of this automatically, without much thought. Robot need every aspect spelled out. If I shouted duck, you'd likely duck. If I shouted duck at a robot, unless programmed correctly, might mean there's a bird.

Depending on the need, purpose and/or chore, a robot should be able to adjust its speed. Running mechanisms are somewhat similar to walking, albeit faster. Under some circumstances wheels might be a better alternative to legs such as a robo-cop racing down a street to catch a bad guy. There are robots these days with both options.

Before launching an ambulatory robot project, there has to be extensive planning, sometimes called solving the piano mover's problem. Envision piano movers carrying an upright piano upstairs through a winding stairwell. Humans automatically make adjustments for every twist and turn, some voluntary, most involuntary, but the humanoid cannot adjust unless it has been properly programmed with every eventuality in mind.

Human replication requires motion-capture studies like those used by military, electronic game makers, movie makers and sports figures. Human actors are sometimes recorded for 3-D images; sampling is done multiple times a second. Every angle has to be studied. Acoustic, inertial, LED lights, magnetic markers are placed at all joints and respective cameras triangulate to capture activity. Variations of these systems were used by the TV series Stargate and the movie The Planet of the Apes.

Humans have the ability to learn from experiences and modify actions. Robots are getting there.

Man Learns New Ways To Move Faster

Man has forever been striving to find ways to move faster and carry heavier loads to farther destinations. At first, the only thing man could do to improve distances was to add foot protection. In the beginning that was animal fur, hides and skins, tied together with primitive strings. This was especially needed in the less temperate regions. Later on, that changed to sandals, shoe-like enclosures and then highly specialized shoes as we have these days. A wooden staff aided climbing. Different kinds of shoes for special occasions, such as certain sports and hiking, are a relatively new phenomenon.

Using pack animals began about eight millennia ago, followed by draft animals that pull rather than carry. The horse was one of those giant steps forward. Later came mules, oxen, reindeer, yaks, donkeys, buffalo, llamas, elephants and camels. Oxen can carry their weight, around one ton, for short distances. Camels can go considerably further and faster, but loads are typically closer to 300 kg or less. Horses and horse-related families carrying capacity tends to be around 20% body weight or 225 pounds. Dogs pull sleds in Arctic areas. A few decades ago, Rottweilers pulled small carts with a single passenger, select luggage and/or goods in Germany.

As it turns out large numbers of horses survived in the Eurasian steppes during the Ice Age. Who actually broke them in (or how) remains unclear, but work by Sandra Olsen, an archaeologist at the Carnegie Museum of Natural History in Pittsburgh, suggests the Botai people of Kazakhstan were first to ride. She has found evidence, dating back to 6000 BC. They used horses for transport, hunting and food. She says[42]" They were our first form of rapid transit." We know that horses were used for carrying soldiers and close-quarter combat years later. The Mongols were known for their accuracy with bow and arrow while riding at a full gallop. This was a striking improvement over the use of bow and arrow from a stationery position.

Domestication of the camel happened around 4500 BC in the southern Arabian Peninsula. They were used as pack animals, mostly to sell incense, and for milk production. Somewhere along the line, blankets were used for saddles. The rider sat between two humps with the load hung evenly on both sides. These animals are well

---

42 William Speed Weed and Philip Newton," First to Ride" March 01, 2002 issue of Discovery magazine .

known for their incredible endurance and ability to travel enormous distances without a need to drink water.

The use of elephants also began about 4000 years ago in the Indus Valley. Their enormous size and strength was valuable for moving very heavy loads and carrying warriors into war. Porus, the Emperor of India, used 85 elephants against Alexander the Great in the Battle of Hydaspes in 326 BC. During the Second Punic War 218-201 BC, Hannibal marched across the Alps to Spain with 35 elephants. His army annihilated the largest army the Romans had ever assembled, estimated to be 67,000 soldiers.

Other animals man has used for riding include the ostrich in Australia, zebra in China, and even the dolphin in the United States. The latter is mostly a tourist attraction.

The discovery of the wheel was a major and enduring effort to improve upon our locomotion. Despite certain publicity, it wasn't Thor, from the Sunday comicstrip BC, who rides a stone unicycle. The actual origin may have been a potter's wheel which was developed in the Near East around 4500 BC. Noted, China and other countries have claimed the same discovery. The earliest well-documented wheel with axle was found in Poland, dated 3340-3030 BCE, but there's also an unclear depiction of a wheeled vehicle dating from the Halaf culture (6500-5100 BCE). The earliest useful wheels were likely made of wood. Much lighter spoked wheels came about 2000 BC. Somewhere mixed in were rolling logs that were probably used to move giant boulders at the Pyramids and Stonehenge. Surely, this must have also triggered some thoughts of wheels.

We know that the wheels in Egyptian chariots were incredibly sophisticated. A team from PBS's Nova[43] series learned how arduous a task really was. This included the precise bending of the right wood, plus balancing and maintaining symmetry (even harder, given

---

43 Building Pharaoh's Chariot PBS/NOVA A team uncovers the advanced engineering behind an ancient Egyptian war machine. Premiered 2/6/13

the tools of the time). Of interest, a number of Roman chariots have been found on a shallow land bridge in the Red Sea where Biblical history says the Romans followed Moses. By the time of Christ's birth, virtually every nation had wheeled vehicles of varied sorts.

The bicycle gave man more speed and distance. The first bicycle belonged to the German Baron Karl von Drais (1817). It was called Laufmaschine which is German for "running machine". The cycle was wooden and quite heavy. It followed the widespread deaths of horses from starvation due to crop failures. His cycle could go about eight miles an hour. The period between 1820 and 1850 brought a plenitude of three and four-wheelers. The word bicycle originated in France 1860s when some versions began to resemble the bike-look as we know it. Improvements such as lighter frames, pneumatic tires, knotting in tires for grip and gearing made bikes increasingly useful, on and off, the road have come about.

The motorcycle followed on the heels of the bicycle. The first steam-powered motorcycle was invented in 1867 by the son of the "velocipede" (bicycles with pedals) inventor, Pierre Michaux, a black-smith in Paris. Soon thereafter an American, Sylvester H. Roper of Roxbury, Massachusetts invented a twin-cylinder version with the coal-fired boiler between the wheels. He died demonstrating the vehicle. I hesitate to think how this (he) might have looked. Cycles with internal combustion and petroleum-fueled evolved in the 1880s and 1890s all over the European and American continent.

The motorized wheelchair was invented by Canadian George Klein to assist veterans who were injured in WWI. It was used by people who could not self-propel themselves and others with easy fatiguability as seen in heart and lung disease. These devices have undergone considerable improvements in the past 100 years. They have more comfortable seats, easy maneuverability and longer-lived batteries. High-end chairs have a stand-up capability wherein the machine actually lifts the user to a standing position with sup-port. Select versions include types for off-road use; some can even negotiate streams, mud, sand, and stairs. What's nice is that paraplegics can fish from a river's side or hunt in the back woods.

Man has also been used as a draft animal. Still is. An unverifiable legend has it that the rickshaw (pedicab) was invented by Jonathan Scobie, an American missionary in Japan, in 1869, to transport his invalid wife. By the 1870s there were about 40,000 rickshaws in Tokyo. The addition of a bicycle was a boom to Chinese society where it eventually became one of three "must-haves" along with the watch and a sewing machine.

Wheels Plus

The wheel underwent slow improvements including improved symmetry, different, enduring spokes and pneumatic tires. Hence the first car, which was brought to market by Karl Benz in 1886. Henry Ford is often sited as the inventor of the car, but his factory was started in 1903. Some of the forerunners were the steam-powered automobile in 1769 by French Army Captain Nicolas-Joseph Cugnot. It could transport four people at a speed of 2.25 miles per hour (brisk walking pace for some). Of note, Ferdinand Verbiest, a Jesuit missionary to China, invented a toy, steam powered vehicle. It was not large enough to carry a person.

In the very early 1800s the first engines running on fuel gas appeared, which led the internal combustion machines. In 1875 the Wisconsin legislature offered a $10,000 award for someone to produce a practical substitute for draft horses. They stipulated this vehicle had to average five mph and complete a 200 mile course. This led to the first auto race in Wisconsin in 1878. Seven vehicles competed, only two finished. The winner made 201 miles in 33 hours and 27 minutes at six mph.

Steam engine were slowly replaced by petrol engines in the late nineteenth century and the beginning of the twentieth century. The first electric car, called the Flocken Elektrowagen, was invented by

Andreas Flocken. Ford was able to reduce the cost of gasoline cars, however, and eased electric cars out of the market. By 1930, electric cars were all, but gone. Two-seaters progressed to four-seaters with pedal control.

Over the past hundred years the changes and improvements in automobiles are too extensive to list, but they include electric starters, windows that became electric, seatbelts, enclosed bodies, improving braking systems, headlights with turn signals, windshield wipers, better tires, heaters, AC, radios, computer screens, adjustable seats, all-wheel drive, fuel-injection, diesel engines, airbags, GPS, increased speed and increase mileage efficiency. And, of course, not the least important, is slots for grande lattes.

Driverless

Was all this aimed at achieving low to zero emissions, driverless cars? I think likely. Without question, many aspects have bled into the development of automated (governed) robots and autonomous (self-governing) robots.

Although we think of driverless vehicles as a very new idea, Leonardo da Vinci gets the credit for being the originator. Around 1478 Leonardo designed a vehicle (actually cart) that was self-propelled by steam and coiled springs. It had "programmable" steering and the ability to drive through a pre-set course. Apparently experts over the next 500 years had trouble understanding how it worked(if it worked). In 2006, Italy's Institute and Museum of the History of science reproduced it. And, it did work.

In the 1920s the linrrican Wonder took its first run. This was a radio-controlled car, controlled by a car behind it. Together they made their way through heavy traffic in New York City. Other radio-controlled vehicles followed. General Motors featured an automated guided car that followed electromagnetic fields embedded in the road. The 1939 World's Fair featured Futurama, a city with super highways and driverless cars. Excited experts predicted this technology would be in common use by mid century, certainly no later than 1975. Market pressures changed all that, however. Gas powered and human-driven cars were considerably cheaper and less complex. The idea of automated cars was not entirely abandoned, however; futuristic models showed up at nearly every car show.

In the 1980s, Mercedes came up with a vision-guided robotic van. Soon thereafter the Autonomous Land Vehicle (ALV)project was able to run an autonomous vehicle using computer vision, GPS and robot control. Using laser lights and radar they could perceive their environment and in some instances follow markers embedded in roadways. Experts[44] predict drastic reductions in accidents (lives saved) and related costs, better traffic flow, restful trips, and lower fuel consumption. Some say crime will be lessened, but this remains to be seen. Finding parking places may be less of a hassle if the car can drop passengers off and return later (when called for or scheduled). Clearly, the disabled and elderly will benefit, gaining significant mobility. In fact, some experts predicted very few city dwellers will own cars. It will cheaper and less hassle to just call companies like Uber and Lyft.

Driverless cars and buses are already on the scene in Taipei, Taiwan. Exercises for a driverless bus called EZ110 were done on the grounds of the National Taiwan University in 2017, transporting as many as twelve passengers. So far, it qualifies for short circuits. It costs over half million dollars and can reach 25 mph. It uses laser sensors, GPS and front and back cameras to avoid obstacles. If proved successful, there is a market for driverless cars transporting millions worldwide.

---

44 Umar Zakir Abdul, Hamid; et al. (2016). "Current Collision Mitigation Technologies for Advanced Driver Assistance Systems–A Survey" (PDF). *PERINTIS eJournal.* **6** (2). Retrieved 14 June 2017. businessinsider.com. 12 September 2014. Retrieved 3 October2014.

In Western Australia, huge driverless trucks help in the mines. They claim that they've driven millions of kilometers and hauled 200 million tonnes of material. Driverless trucks are also being used in Chile. Use of these trucks eliminates the fatigue factor seen with human drivers.

The military is also interested. There's a fleet of "zombie trucks (at last check) at Fort Hood with plans to use these groups to save lives of personnel. The Sartre project in Europe is rolling driverless lorries through Spain. Apparently, this is safer, more environmental friendly and optimal for supervision. They travel at set speeds and keep a specific distance apart. There's no need to stop for naps.

So, when will driverless cars be ready for use? That's not clear, but there's a lot of excitement surrounding these projects. For one, the US alone incurs 40,000 highway deaths a year and 1.2 million worldwide. Plus. there's hundreds of thousands who are seriously injured. Authorities presently suspect that one-fourth of all drivers are impaired by drugs, medications or alcohol, too drowsy for a variety of reasons, or too old or infirm with dangerously slow reflexes. Think of that when you're driving 70 mph down a highway. A drunk or a senior citizen who thinks he/she still can fly at 80mph may be driving toward you.

More than half a million lines of code will power the various systems and algorithms that could one day help self-driving cars go anywhere. That includes localization systems, overlaid with high-definition maps to help the vehicles understand where they are. And, perception systems, which help vehicles determine exactly what's going on around them.

Yet, there have been several accidents that have slowed the advancement of driverless cars. By 2015, there had been 11 non-fatal accidents over six years. Humans are a threat, in particular pedestrians, cyclists and road workers. They are not always visible and can act in unexpected ways. Bad weather can interfere with the function of these cars. What will happen with ice, or any slippery surface, cannot be known. Snow and rain can blind sensors or distort messaging. Given two simultaneous crises is often cited as an example. What if a car has to stop short to avoid striking someone, a child, but that may cause a dangerous pile-up behind? Can a machine decide how to handle this in a nanosecond? There definitely is a need for new laws for these vehicles. There are many scenarios that have not even been imagined at this time.

The Uber accident in Tempe that killed the first pedestrian in March 2018 stands out. A hard to watch video showing a lady crossing the street with grocery bags. The sensors in the car should have picked her up, but for some unknown reason they didn't. The car did stop after striking her, for whatever that's worth. The passenger helper or assistant was glancing down at her lap and apparently didn't react in time as she was supposed to.

Cortica, a company that develops autonomous artificial intelligence, analyzed the video. Their system detected the pedestrian at 0.9 second before impact when the car was about 50 feet away. Had the car reacted(braked), she would be alive today. Tempe police said the car didn't brake or swerve and it struck her going 38 mph. Some say driverless cars should all have a blue light warning others. This color can be seen by those who are color blind.

It's unknown when this technology will completely kick in. Even if one million driverless cars were be made each year (an industry guess), that will only be one percent of the total cars we make and buy. Chaning over may take several decades. That is, once we really start.

Non-Human Locomotion

One of the first automatons with moving extremities was invented by the 13th century engineer Al-Jarri. Illustrations show that there were four robotic musicians in a boat, two drummers, one harpist and flutist. Arms were made to move by a rotating cylindrical beam with cams (pegs). It was displayed at gala events.

Leonardo Da Vinci is given enormous credit for a robotic man with the invention of a mechanical knight in 1495. Using a series of pulleys, cranks and gears, it could sit, stand, lift its visor and move its head. It was shown at gala events in Milan for Duke Ludovico Sforza.

Throughout the Renaissance Period clockmakers across Europe got into the act, making a number of famous clockworks with automata. Wind up toys have also mimicked man's capabilities. One toy could walk downhill(only), driven by the pull of gravity.

Honda began developing humanoids that could walk in the 1980s. EO was one of the first bipedal prototypes. The Honda P series followed through the 1990s, resulting in the ASIMO robot which was unveiled in 2000. The acronym stands for Advanced Step in Innovative Mobility and it could walk on two legs, recognize moving objects, understand voice commands, and interpret a wave or handshake.

Standing 130 cm (4 ft 3 in) and weighing 54 kg (119 pounds), ASIMO is all white, except for a dark black, face mask. It was powered by a rechargeable 51.8 lithium-ion battery which lasted about an hour. Later this was changed to nickel metal hydride in 2004 which improved times needed for recharging. ASIMO could walk at 9 kph and maintained good balance. Ultimately, it played soccer with President Obama and appeared on TV with Kelly Ripa.

ASIMO has since been retired, but Honda has gone onto physical therapy and self-driving cars, starting with UNI-CUB and the Walking Assist. The former is a personal mobility device with saddle that travels by leaning forward or turns with body shifts. The later device goes around the lower body and attaches to both upper legs to aid walking, climbing stairs, and staying in a semi-crouching position for the elderly and disabled. Learned technologies have gone into their motorcycles and cars. After the Fukushima meltdown, Honda has created a robot that can inspect nuclear power plants.

More and more robots are walking, jumping, running and rolling. The fastest, by far, are those that roll. The HANDLE Robot, developed by Boston Dynamics, is a vertical robot that looks a little like a wild horse rearing up on its hind limbs. It stands 6.5 feet, travels at 9 mph and can jump 4 feet vertically. Google it for You Tube viewing. It can roll faster than anyone can walk or run. It is called a nightmare. It looks scary and a human cannot get away from it.

Boston Dynamic's SpotMini is a robot dog with four legs It has a square head with camera eyes, and an arm that comes over from the back that that can open doors. It can walk, run, dance, walk backwards, climb steps, follow commands and turn 360 degrees. It walks over obstacles and can get into areas that robots with wheels cannot. It can also build a 3D map and use it to navigate on it's own. Boston Dynamics has a robot that can run and do flips. It's hard to imagine the benefit.

The military has developed a robot pack mule that can easily walk through rough terrain. In some ways it resembles metal ox. This is DARPA's semiautonomous Legged Squad Support System, aka the L53. It can carry 400 pounds of warfighter equipment and walk 20 miles at a time. A soldier can only carry 100 pounds. It can navigate at night and follow ten basic, voice commands such as follow me closely.

In a paper[45] presented at the Living Machines 2017 conference, scientists showed how fallen robots could right themselves with a maneuver similar to click beetles. A study done by Dr Kyu-Jin Cho, at the University of Illinois, describes and analyzes the stages a click beetle does to right itself when it has fallen on its back. The insect is considered two body masses attached by a hinge and using high-speed video recordings and scanning electron micrographs of four beetle species, they have come up with a framework to help robotics.

45 Bolmin O. et al. (2017) Pop! Observing and Modeling the Legless Self-righting Jumping Mechanism of Click Beetles. In: Mangan M., Cutkosky M., Mura A., Verschure P., Prescott T., Lepora N. (eds) Biomimetic and Biohybrid Systems. Living Machines 2017. Lecture Notes in Computer Science, vol 10384. Springer, Cha.

Human Locomotion

We all take walking and running for granted. Unless a person finds oneself in a precarious situation, perhaps post injury or stroke, very little attention is paid to placing one foot in front of the other and pushing off with the back foot. Yet, somehow the feet seem to know what to do, when and how fast.

Lower extremities have to be specific for the species. If all birds were flat footed like ducks, they would be falling from trees right and left. Eagles could not grab salmon from the rivers. And, bats would be dropping from the ceilings of caves.

We are a bipedal, meaning a moving two-legged species that is capable of crawling, walking, running, skipping, jumping, jogging, hopping, running, sprinting, moving to either side, turning 360 degrees, moving sideways and walking backwards. While we maintain a center of balance, we stay attentive to our surroundings. Vision and hearing, and often touch, are commonly engaged. With rare exceptions, we don't run into trees or walk off cliffs. There is a slightly different gait between genders. Women tend to take smaller steps and have a greater pelvic swing. And, there are gait changes as we age, forced by skeletal changes and less muscle strength.

Arm swinging with human bipedal walking is a natural motion. Each arm swings at the same time the opposing leg steps forward. This improves balance. Although this pendulum motion is not critical, it improves balance and is more energy efficient.

Varied, yet specific, joint actions are critical to ambulation. In mammals these are the hips, knees, and ankles as well as certain joints in the foot. Try keeping your balance without using your toes. Try dancing with stiff ankles. Try walking upstairs with a stiff hip. All joints are fluid-filled which aids easy movement and this viscous fluid acts as a buffer helping to lessen injury to the ends of bones. Note the tips of bones also are cupped with cartilage to aid smooth movement. This, too, lessens injury.

The hips have a classic ball-in-socket arrangement, allowing our legs to swing forward (flex) and back (extend) as well as swivel. There's no purpose to having the same kind of joint at the knee or ankle, in fact, it would a dangerous waste of genetic time. Indeed, there's no evidence nature ever tried this by trial and error. The knee is hinge-like and moves back and forth; the ankle is complex, mostly designed for up and down movements. Three major joints all different, all appropriate, none with previous problematic systems. And, so has been everything needed to make them work. Muscles are situated to work together, often opposing each other for balanced strength. Otherwise one muscle might pull the extremity to the far end and leave it there.

The pelvis acts as a primary support for the weight of the body as well as a fulcrum and an anchor. This is a combination of three fused bones (unfused or partially fused would not work) with two, strategically situated sockets for the hip "balls". Put your fist inside your other cupped hand and moved it about. That should give you the idea.

All left-sided parts come as a complimentary match to the right-sided parts. Muscles are placed very specifically to maximize strength and torque. There are ones to pull that leg forward or back, to go sideways, and others there specifically for rotation. Tendons keep these muscles tightly attached to strategic spots on the bone around the joint. Ligaments keep the ball and socket together, reinforce the structure). Specific nerves inform or direct all parts to function properly together. Specific arteries, never random ones, bring nutrients and oxygen while specific parallel veins remove carbon dioxide and metabolic products. It's a bit like an Interstate highway with two lanes going coming and two lanes going.

Note balance is also affected by every joint, yet control of the balance mechanisms is in the brain.

The knees are the perfect hinge joints (like a door, but horizontal). They are the largest and may be the most complicated joints we have. Each knee joint securely connects the large femur bone with

152

the two thinner bones (the tibia and fibula) below. Try sitting down in a chair without bending your knees. Better yet, try getting up. What if they didn't always or couldn't, lock? They'd give way whenever you took a step. The joint has to be extremely strong to balance one's weight. All this smacks of purpose and design.

Both knees have ligaments to reinforce their positions as do many joints. The kneecap protects the joint from injuries incurred by falling forward. A cartilaginous, inner lining protects the bone ends from banging against each other and wearing down. Fluid inside the knee cushions all actions. Strategically placed muscles flex and extend the knee and help it twist in and out. Tendons anchor muscles to bones and ligaments help stabilize the joint.

The ankle is actually three joints that work mostly as a hinge allowing the foot to dorsiflex and plantar-flex (bring the foot up or down). It also supports body weight One main role is the push off while walking. This joint has four major, very strong ligaments and is controlled by muscles. Nerves and blood, like all aspects of the body, supply and service these joints.

The human foot is truly unique. It is geared for walking, running, jumping, gait thrust, weight bearing and maintaining balance. Some of us can pick-up socks with our toes and a few unfortunate individuals, who are missing their upper extremities, have learned to feed themselves, write, care for their children, and even paint with their toes. There are 26 bones and 33 joints there, plus a system of tendons, similar to hands. Together they carry out a wide range of flexion and extension at varying strengths.

There are two basic phases to our walking: stance and swing. These can be further broken down into heel strike, early flatfoot, late flatfoot, heel rise and toe off. People who lose their smallest toe, rarely notice a change, but the loss of a big toe can have a significant impact that often requires extra training, i.e. physical therapy.

We take walking, running, stepping up on a curb, walking down stairs, and jumping across puddles for granted, but ask someone who's had a stroke or a spinal injury how hard it was to relearn the simplest tasks of walking. We do these maneuvers without any thought. The blueprints are ingrained, automatically drawn on as toddlers. Our feet and ankle act as a lever and the bones in the foot act somewhat like gears. It's all coordinated. Note how horses and dogs beautifully run on all fours. Or, insects with six or eight extremities. Incredible coordination is taking place and it's doubtful animals give it any thought. And so, it probably goes with centipedes and millipedes.

The spinal column consists of 33 vertebrae, divided (top to bottom) into cervical, thoracic, lumbar, sacrum and coccyx or tailbone. Think of a secured stack of boxes. The top 24 vertebrae have pad-like discs located between each to act as shock absorbers. They form a wave-like configuration to lessen shock. The entire column is secured by very tight muscles, tendons and ligaments which help keep us vertical, yet they also allow us to turn sideways, bend back and bend forward with relative ease.

The upper vertebrae also encircle, and thereby protect, by creating a bony channel around a pipeline of long nerves (spinal cord). Like telephone or electrical lines to every house these nerves will travel to all parts of the body. There are trillions (+) targets. These bones also act as a vertical closet that supports (anchors) the ("hanging") organs like the heart, lungs, liver, spleen, adrenal glands, kidneys and the entire digestive tract. The spinal column runs from the base of the skull to the pelvis. And, no, we don't have tails. Never really did. Science has not shown how tails disappeared with evolution. Was there a God of the Gaps at work, Intelligent Guidance?

The human pelvis is located where people incorrectly sometimes say their hips are found and from there it makes a full circle. Women incorrectly say their hips are too wide, pointing to the sides or back of the pelvic area, but technically the hips are on both sides of the groin. Nonetheless, this circular arrangement of bones connects , and stabilizes, the upper body with the lower extremities. They also protect the reproductive organs, the bladder and rectum like a wrap-around shield might.

Most human babies start crawling by 4 months and stand by 9 to 10 months. They take first steps by 12 months and walk by 18 months. This is an entirely normal progression, almost predictable down to the week these start. The simple process of standing up is not actually simple, let alone taking that first step. Nearly all aspects of the brain's motor area are used for ambulation. Not only is the thought to get up and move need to be present, but the muscles, bones, ligaments and tendons need to be strong enough to carry out the maneuver. No need trying when the skeleton is not ready. And, don't forget the ability of the hands and arms to grab onto furniture.

The process of walking breaks down into lifting one leg, pushing forward with the other leg, swinging the lifted leg to the front, falling forward onto the forward leg which should soon be touching the ground, and then repeat the same processes with the other leg. And then, there's the foot strike, whether it should be forefoot, mid-foot or heel first, and weight shifting forward, all focusing on one's center of gravity.

Without maturation of these processes humans, or any species, could never have found food, escaped predators, run down prey and found partners to procreate.

The Prosthetics and Cyborg Piece

The first known prosthetic device was a wooden big toe, called the "Cairo Toe." It was attached by a string to a mummified foot. It probably belonged to a noble woman between 950-719 BC. Close examination suggests it could have been used while barefoot or wearing the traditional sandals. The first prosthetic leg is called the "Capua Leg". The medical practice of amputation can be traced back to a medical text "On Joints" by Hippocrates. Although many occurred on the battlefield, amputations were used as a punishment for thievery and ritual sacrifices. Most recipients died. Knowledge of sterile technique was centuries away. Prostheses date back to Capua, Italy, about 300 BC. A replica shows a wooden prosthesis supposedly worn by Götz von Berlich, a Franconian Knight who lost his arm in battle about 1504. There's confusion, however. The piece is a left arm and history says he lost his right arm.

Wooden legs, sometimes called peg legs, may go back into prehistory. Every battle has left many warriors without extremities and history is replete with efforts to find a functional substitute. Some missing arms and hands were replaced with a variety of cosmetic devices that were rarely functional. The Roman General Marcus Sergius, used a prosthetic iron hand to hold his shield. Ambroise Paré, a sixteenth century French surgeon-barber drastically improved amputation procedures and created several prosthetic devices. He showed that the practice of adding oils to new wounds and cautery made the prognosis worse. He was the first (known) to tie off arteries.

A Dutch surgeon, Pieter Verduyn, created a non-locking, knee prosthesis in 1696. In 1800, James Potts of London developed an articulated knee-and-foot prosthesis. An apprentice of Potts, William Selpho, procured a patent (No. 18021), called the Artificial Hand. It had a loop around the opposite shoulder which could affect the grip. Cat tendons were used to move fingers. Leather wove its way in and out of use in the past few centuries and include a very interesting prosthetic foot from India that fits like a closed shoe.

Prosthetic legs did not change significantly until the later 1800s, but surgical improvements tended toward shaping stumps for a better fit into artificial limbs. Our Civil War left an incredible number of amputees, estimated to be 70,000. Photos show areas outside surgical tents with stacks of amputated limbs, like a slash pile. Aware of the horror, the Federal government initiated the Great Civil War Benefaction program and many manufacturing groups responded with a host of improvements. Rubber was substituted for certain parts, making limbs more flexible, lighter and more resilient. James Hanger, a confederate soldier with an amputated leg, went on to develop a helpful limb, known as the "Hanger Limb." His was made with barrel staves and had hinged joints at the knee and ankle. Hanger's company lingers today.

Despite the carnage of several world wars, advancements in prosthetic devices remained limited before the last hundred years. Certain protheses were specific for industries having attachments for hammers and other tools. In 1946 UC Berkeley researchers developed a suction cup which is still used today. Another amputee Ysidro M. Martinez improved functions of gait and reduced friction. In recent times there have been major strides. Carbon fibers, advancements in biometrics and 3D printing have made prosthetics lighter, stronger and more functional. We also can surgically implant joints, lessening the need for some amputations. Metal fixtures can reinserted in and along extremity severely injured bones. Hinge technology has taken replacements into finger and toe joints.

Dean Kamen, inventor of the Segway, was awarded approval by the U. S. F. D. A. for an arm prosthesis that uses electrodes that read muscle movement and converts the initial brain waves into action. Using vibrations the fingers can sense how soft an item might be. They can actually pick a grape from a bunch. DARPA has invested $100 million and 399 scientists in these kinds of program. Some of the people involved are amputees, themselves, supporting the idea that necessity is often the mother of all inventions.

Bionic eyes are restoring partial sight. Cochlear implants are returning hearing to many hearing-impaired. Breast reconstruction has developed adequate substitutes, Cosmetic surgery has prosthetic chins, cheeks and butts.

Bionic limbs now have microprocessors and electrodes that sense muscle movement. They come with capabilities to change grips including tying shoes and can be stylish as seen by the model Rebekah Marine who was born with an absent right lower arm. Daniel

Bastian, also reported by the New York Post, October 25, 2015, has a multipurpose leg prosthesis following an amputation for bone cancer. He can use it for swimming, biking and walking by tapping the heel in a select way (produced by the German company Ottobock). Another victim, Shannon Smith incurred a quadruple amputation in 2011 from infection complications (sepsis) of pregnancy. She has near normal function of her upper extremities from prostheses produced by Ottobock and robotic knees provided by Icelandic company Össur. Her hand can close soft and hard. She says that the sensations, using her own muscles, feels near-normal.

By 2021, one in three surgeries in the US will be done by robotic arm(s) with the operating surgeon sitting at a computer console, located anywhere from a few feet away to thousands of miles away. By 2030, it will become the standard of care. The robotic procedure allows for more complex procedures to be done in less invasive ways. State of the art is the da-Vinci X-1. Reports indicate blood loss, less post-op pain, and quicker recoveries, These machines can stitch a peeled grape back together, but they are not entirely benign. There can be equipment malfunctions, patient injuries and even deaths. Time will tell how they compare to older methods. These telemedicine procedures can be done virtually with 5G, gloves and a VR headset.

The world's first robotic kitchen can be operated by a touch screen or remotely by a smart phone. Paired articulated hands reproduce the entire function of human hands with similar speed, sensitivity, and movement. This is to be launched by MOLEY and it is the combined work of Shadow Robotics, Yachtline, DYSEGNO, Sebastian Conran and Stanford University Professor Mark Cutkosky. Two robotic arms/hands descend to the stove and cook with the ambidexterity and touch of a master chef. Robotic arms are now making alcoholic drinks along the Miracle Mile in Las Vegas and coffee at Cafe X in San Francisco.

Robotic arms are being used in paralyzed victims. Nathan Copeland an American, who lost all sensation from the chest down after his car skidded off a highway ten years before, became the first to use a sensory-enhanced robotic hand. Wires were surgically inserted in his brain so that he could feel and operate the hand with his brain waves. Copeland reported the hand had an "almost" natural feel. Blindfolded he had an 84% accuracy when reporting the hand was touched and 93% accuracy describing the item.

Another interesting case is Ian Burkhart who received a neural bypass, a brain implant developed by a charity called Battelle[46], that could send messages to the paralyzed muscles in his arm and hand. As a result he can play certain video games, including Guitar Hero, hold a phone to his ear and stir a cup of coffee. His first movements by thought happened in 2014. This will become a huge asset.

Both industry and military have been particularly interested in exoskeletal power augmentation units to aid workers on production lines when true robotic arms cannot do the job. These devices are worn across the upper or lower torso with attachments to the extremities. They are sensitive to the user's intentions. If one bend forwards, he/she starts to walk; if a person turns, it turns. In some situations the user can lift much more than they could without the exoskeleton.

The thought that individual can be part machine and part human(bionic) seemed far fetched in the past, but may seem more realistic now. Complex, responsive extremity prosthetics, newer manufacturing methods and newer composites have moved us closer to bionic people or cyborgs.

In 2012 Teddy Ward a five year old suffered a traumatic head injury when he fell down a cliff in Topanga Canyon, near Los Angeles. He lost half of his skull and an attempt to replace his skull failed. He had to wear a helmet for two years and had strikingly limited activities, fearing he could suffer severe brain damage if he were

---

46 Chad E. Bouton, et al, *Quadriplegia,*" *Nature* volume 533, 247–250 (12 May 2016) doi:10.1038/nature17435.

to fall. In 2014, however doctors at Children's Hospital Los Angeles (CHLA) using 3-D printing were able to replace the damaged area with PolyEtherEtherKetone (PEEK). This material isn't plastic and has similar physical properties as a skull. Other than contact sports like football, he was able to resume all normal activities. Implants of these sorts may eventually be able to replace ninety percent any bony structures in the future.

Researchers at Ohio State University have been working on a brain implant that helps quadriplegics use their extremities with thoughts. The electrode can read the individual's mind to move the arm and electrodes on that arm will help it do that function. Patients have been able to do such things as swipe a credit card, play Guitar Hero, and stir cream and sugar in a drink. Just think it and could happen

Prosthetics have also moved into the animal world as well with thousands fitted yearly. Seen on a PBS[47] special a pony named Molly who survived hurricane Katrina and a dog attack now walks quite well with a front leg prosthesis. She meets regularly with handi-capped children, some of whom have prostheses. There is a golden retriever with a front leg prosthesis that goes to hospitals and visits children. A small pig called Chris P. Bacon has an animal wheelchair replacing his rear legs. We now see this wheelchair commonly being utilized by paraplegic dogs. The video also showed a swan, who lost part of its upper beak to a snapping turtle, receiving a functional replacement, and an alligator getting a tail which helped it swim.

Over the past hundred years man has made giant strides in these areas. This is far beyond the fictional (and true) peg legs and hooks for hands. It appears as if the mechanisms controlling robotic artifi-cial walking and hand grips have borrowed from prosthetic devices. Some are for cosmetic purposes such as artificial eyes, breast implants, butt implants, chin extenders, higher cheeks and dental

---

47 PBS video: "My Bionic Pet" (April 9, 2014) www.pbs.org/wnet/nature/my-bionic-pet-my-bionic-pet/8696

implants. Others are present to restore function, some even improve capabilities.

Exoskeletons For Humans

Nature is very aware of the benefit of exoskeletons. This might be called a body shell, design to look like the body area covered, maybe a modern day knight's armor made of lighter materials. This kind of shielding can protect the body within, but more so, it can also be used as a strength-multipliers. How strong might a shell-less crab be without it? How safe? Or, an insect? These animals would be wiggling clumps of protoplasm. We now have fictional versions of a power-loader bit like the one used by Ellen Ripley in the movie Aliens to fight a larger, stronger, more fit foe.

New developments in exoskeletons are also helping paraplegic human patients walk. In the past, these patients, like those with cerebral palsy(CP), were bedridden and/or confined to wheelchairs, but the ability to walk around like the rest of us do is on the flat. Recently, Suit X won $1M top prize in the International Robotics for Good Competition in Dubai. They beat out 664 other entrants with a 27 lb, adjustable exoskeleton for children born with CP or spina bifida. The medical exoskeleton (Phoenix) is already helping people with mobility disorders and the industrial exoskeleton(MAX) reduces industrial injuries in workers who do highly intensive jobs.

EksoGT is an exoskeleton that has been approved to help patients with strokes or spinal injuries walk again. It was changed from military applications to use by millions of people in wheelchairs. These are basically motorized braces. They are near full body-length with straps over the shoulder with the batteries and microprocessors found in a metal box in the back. These can be adjusted for thigh length. Metal support rods go down behind both legs and attach to the thighs. The foot is a narrow platform with an ankle dorsiflexor (brings the foot up). A variation can help workers handle heavy lifts and overhead work. Military versions are more durable, heavier and sometimes waterproof. These are quite expensive now and primarily used in rehab centers, but there are expectations to have these available soon for individual users at better prices.

The Human Universal Load Carrier (HULC) from Lockheed is a third generation anthropomorphic exoskeleton for soldiers and certain climbers and hikers. It is lightweight made with titanium. The user straps it over his shoulders, at the waist and to the legs. A microprocessor determines where the wearer wants to go or do. The user can bend, run, walk, squat, crawl, turn. It can help carry up to 200 pounds (front and back) and decreases the wearer's metabolic cost, meaning it increases endurance and lowers the oxygen needs. Using it for fighting inrough terrains like the Afghan mountains would give a major advantage. It only weighs 52 pounds, but it takes care of that extra load. A suited-up soldier can walk about 7 mph while the exoskeleton helps the soldier run 10 mph. It can be adjusted for heights 5-4 to 6-2 and can be removed in less than 30 seconds.

Human Upper Extremity

Someone, somewhere, somehow realized there's no need to stick one's finger(s) into a boiling pot when a stick could do the work a lot easier and not create painful blisters. That said, hands have been, and still are in some societies, the only utensils used for millennia.

History texts say chopsticks, often cited as the first machines, were invented 9000 years ago and were likely used for cooking, stirring and moving food. As food became smaller and chopped (ergo "chopsticks"), the need for a tweezer-like action became apparent. The customary clumpy and sticky rice also lended itself to a pair of sticks. In addition, Confucius, a known vegetarian, believed that if sharp utensils were added to a meal it would remind diners of violence; he suggested that mealtime be more peaceful.

Nowadays, the knife and fork are the utensils of choice in most Western civilization homes. The first fork appeared in ancient Egypt and had two tines. Ancient Greeks used knives and spoons to eat. A pointed, sharp knife worked like a fork for many. Bone forks have been found among several cultures dating 1000-2000 BC. Tines vary widely in length. Archaeologists have found bronze forks from eighth century Persian sites. Legend has an ancient Byzantine princess criticized for not wanting to touch her food. She used a kind of fork, instead. A forward thinker? In later centuries Italians added more tines, discovering that a few twists of a fork was much more efficient and less much sloppy than when using a spoon for spaghetti.

Man has quickly learned that hand tools (aka hand-extenders) can improve work outcomes, save time and lessen the load. Many of these tools are now taken for granted, but each was a significant invention in its time. Also, they were an advancement toward the robotic world. Other advances include hammers, screwdrivers, axes, pliers, saws, knives, scalpels, hand-grippers, pitchforks, shovels, combs, toothpicks, hairbrushes and toothbrushes. The first power tool was invented in 1895 when the German engineering company C&E combined an electric motor with a manual drill. To make life easier and work more efficient, hand tools have progressed to automatic versions. Note the shift for loggers cutting redwoods. The next step will be telling an android handyman to do the fixing, drilling, or chopping.

Our hands are masterfully designed, fit for a creature that needs to write, type, play a musical instrument, sew clothes, hitchhike, twist tools, caress, pray, tie ties, thread a needle, operate and build things like robots—**among many, many, many things that other mammals cannot do.** Imagine our lives with two to four fins, paws, claws, hooves or some combo, instead of hands. Or, maybe long arms so we can knuckle walk?

It is readily apparent that our lives are much easier as designed. And, noted we came this way from our very start. There are no findings of incomplete humans. Or, for that matter, incomplete monkeys. Human hands come as mirror-images. It's difficult to imagine hands coming any other way. In fact, they never have. There are no fossils or old skeletons with thumbs (or their counterparts) located elsewhere on the hand. Or, with both palms facing different directions, such as outward. Or, drastically different sizes as seen in some crabs and certain beetles.

Even if an ape could type on a computer, they lack the wiring in their brain to make any sense of it. In 2003, Six macaque monkeys (Elmo, Gum, Heather, Holly, Mistletoe, and Rowan) were given a computer at the Paignton Zoo in Devon to see if they might demonstrate any hint that monkeys, given infinite time, could type any part of Shakespeare's works. Instead, they produced five pages of nonsensical typing, which was mostly S's. and a lot of poop on the machines. One might argue that there weren't enough monkeys and not enough time, but the answer is a resounding: there would be too much poop to see any useful manuscripts.

Opposable thumbs, which means the ability to touch the other fingers on the same hand, are remarkably useful, especially when grasping and using tools. Monkeys and humans have always been known to have this skill, but we know now octopuses can do similar tasks by bending tentacles and suckers in unison or selectively. Humans can play musical instruments, such as the piano, where the fingers are moving in different, yet interactive ways. These tasks would be virtually impossible for other animals to accomplish.

Having ten fingers and ten toes may be the best functional design. Note five is a Fibonacci number. We know that persons with a sixth finger (or toe) generally find it awkwardly placed and rarely useful. Some parents have it removed while an infant. Twelve fingers on both hands might be ok, but it seems to be a waste when five on each will do. Physicians know that human grip offered by five fingers is stronger than that of four or less. Consider their useful when counting and/or communicating with sign language. Using systems of ones, twos, fives and tens may be the simplest way to go. Obviously, the designers of the abacus liked the system.

Egyptian hieroglyphics made use of different parts of the human anatomy to send messages. Arms raised high and elbows bent in an obtuse angle meant rejoice. The finger in the mouth was a child. The arms forming three sides of a rectangle with forearms parallel was the soul. We do the same with nonverbal language. What does it mean if someone is facing you with their arms folded, plus they have a stern look? Or, a fist held high or both hands flat together?

The few muscles found in the hands are there more to make the hairs stand up when we're stressed. Fingers are worked by tendons, sliding back and forth under slippery, inverted V-shaped channels. In a sense, our digits are extensions from muscles and worked like puppets on strings. Note the fingers moving as a clarinetist plays. There are 17 muscles in the palm and 18 in the forearm that do most of our hand work and they do our work most often without any thought. To see, just for fun, see how many silent gestures you can make with one or more fingers.

Joints in our fingers (and sometimes toes) are geared to bend (sometimes grip), flex and extend. Fingerprints (and toe-prints) on the inner tips are actually ridges for better gripping. They are exquisitely sensitive as noted by Braille users. One can debate the value of nails which is the equivalent of tusks, horns, and hooves. Standout explanations include simple protection, scratching a lover's back, scratching an attacker, scratching that itch, and removing ticks.

Every hand (paw, claw) needs and an extension part to reach out and do whatever work is needed. Interestingly, the span of a person's outspread arms, from the tip of the longest finger on one hand to the equivalent finger on the other hand, generally matches one's height. The Greek Freak (Giannis Antetokounmpo) of the Milwaukee Bucks basketball team stands a hair under seven feet and has a symmetric, seven-foot three arm span. According to Da Vinci the width of the hand equals the smallest width of your foot. The distance between the elbow and the wrist equals one's foot length. The distance of forearm plus hand to forearm approaches the Golden Ratio.

Our arms are complementary matches which makes activities such as lifting, swimming, fighting, carrying, swinging a baseball bat and hugging easier. Those unfortunates who are born with only one useful limb or endured an amputation can vouch for the difficulties. Different muscle groups are recruited by the brain, depending on the task. Imagine trying to figure out what muscles and joints must you need just before every activity, and making all changes, all day long. This , I believe, comes compliments of Design and Foresight.

Quadrillions of muscle cells work together and/or in opposition. Every motion has at least two opposing muscles groups controlling the action. Billions of very specific nerves feed these cells simultaneous information. Uncountable numbers of minute arterioles bring the oxygen and nutrients that are needed and take the metabolic products away. When not in use, they all assume a comfortable position, neutral between flexion and extension (idling).

"Now, I know there's a God in heaven!"

ALBERT EINSTEIN, 1930, SAID AFTER HEARING VIOLINIST
YEHUDI MENUHIN AFTER HIS CONCERT WITH THE BERLIN
PHILHARMONIC ORCHESTRA, 1930.

XI
The Protective Covering Piece

How would it be if all of "God's" creatures lacked a protective covering? Even submicroscopic viruses have a specific capsule surrounding their DNA or RNA matrix. Microscopic organisms have much more specific and elaborate cell walls with a host of loading docks, convoluted passageways, different-sized highways and highly varied carrier mechanisms.

Skin or an equivalent protects us from the environments. It helps regulate our inner temperatures, keeping us cooler in the summer and warmer in the winter. It offers more than just aesthetic value. In many cases it provides camouflage. Since many animals don't share the same range of vision, what might stand out for our eyes on a prairie or grassy plain, like a zebra, might be somewhat hidden from others.

Coverings help keep everything inside from falling out. Surgeons sometimes find our guts suddenly popping out after making a midline incision in the abdomen. Evaporation or the loss of fluids is controlled by sweat pores that can open and close as needed, releasing or retaining sweat (fluid). The lack of control can be seen in unfortunate patients with extensive body burns who can lose life-threatening amounts of fluids on a daily basis. Before the advent of IV fluids, many died quickly from severe dehydration.

Aesthetics, without saying, are extremely important. It goes without saying, no skin (also, odd eyes, minimal facial features), equals no loving attraction. How might one identify an arriving family member at Reagan National Airport if no one had skin? Name tags? How would you pick out your own child playing basketball, without a number on the jersey?

Robot Covering And Support

Obviously, robots need an exterior, too. In this situation their exterior may also be a major supporting structure; skin and various hides have no such benefit Choices include wood, plastic, sheet metal or composites. The decision is based on suitability, cost and availability to goals. Wood may be the cheapest product and it is relatively easy to procure, but, there's easy wear and tear and maybe splinters with handshakes. No one wants a robot whose face is warped. If robots become the firefighters in the future, wooden applicants are likely to be denied.

Plastic is another material that can be used. It is relatively cheap, comes in many forms and can easily be molded into a variety of desired shapes. It may also be easier to work with than wood. Having robots that melt under intense heat doesn't play well. Metal is the classic covering. Granted, it might be more difficult to mold, more costly and heavier, but clearly has advantages for rugged outdoors work. If the goal is to make a humanoid, it's hard to make a metal robot feel like a human being. Composites are probably the best options. Much of this is discussed earlier.

One would think that humanoids should have a skin like surface. Noted, there are five root-races, however, and dozens of different skin tones. Might freckles and dimples add to the deception? Maybe, a scar over one eyebrow or along the chin?

An "electric" robot skin has already been developed by Georgia Tech which may help individuals with prosthetic arms and could even give robots capabilities that approximate ours. A new kind of piezotronic transistor mesh acts like skin using thousands of nano-wired transistors. Whenever these are touched an electric current, meaning message, is created.

In 2015, Tolley and Bartlett working with Harvard University and UC San Diego reported creating the first robot with a 3-D printed body that was soft to the touch. Soft robots are much more aesthetic. In testing this version it hopped more than 100 times and endured 35 falls from a height of almost four feet without sustaining damage whereas the rigid metal version only survived a total of 5 falls. According to Bartlett, robots with mixed rigidity may be versatile in dangerous search-and-rescue operations and work on alien planets. These characters can bend, adapt and withstand more hostile environments.

Living Coverings In General

Most bacteria ("germs") like streptococcus and diphtheria are contained within a gel-like capsule. It often helps the bacteria adhere to their target cells, like our throat lining. In select bacteria their interior is not as well organized and is more loosely contained by a slime layer.

Macroscopic (larger) organisms are divided into vertebrates (with a spine or backbone) and invertebrates (without a spine or backbone). The latter is the most diverse group of animals on Earth, estimated to cover 95-97% of all species. Examples found on land include spiders, scorpions, worms and insects, while huge numbers (like, corals, sponges, starfish, clams, squid, jellyfish) are also found in our seas. All are cold-blooded. Some have a radial symmetry, like a clam; others are somewhat amorphous like an octopus. According to the theory of evolution, some of these spineless animals are predecessors to fish and all land animals (with a spine). How they could, by evolution, add DNA instructions by accident is unknown.

An insect's outer surface or exoskeleton is made of chitin. This is actually two layers: the epicuticle which is waxy and water resistant, and the inner layer called the pro-cuticle which also has two layers. Variations in this layers can be seen among members of the group. Butterflies have muscles attached that move their wings while spiders use hydraulic pressures that move their legs. There are many changes that lack logical explanations.

Because the exoskeleton on insects is rigid, tight and hard, insects cannot grow unless they shed the old covering and secrete a new one. The process is called molting and it comes about in steps or stages. It doesn't fit an evolution scheme. Availability of food and weather can impact the timing of these stages. Designed?

Before the exterior shell is removed, the epidermis pulls away from the exoskeleton; a gel is secreted into the created space which will form the next exoskeleton. Enzymes in the gel help break down and split the skeleton along the back. Wings do not appear until the last step. None of this is a coincidence or accident.

Skin keeps all of our interiors tucked in and the outdoors out. Without it, we'd all resemble crispy prunes. It comes in varying degrees of toughness, often based on thickness, and varying degrees of permeability.

Amphibian skin is scales and moist. It can also be permeable to water; these animals can actually breathe through their skin, called cutaneous respiration. Notably, a frog's skin is very vascular, so as to better absorb oxygen. That permeability allows them to hibernate at the bottom of bodies of water. The Bornean flat-headed frog has no lungs or gills and breathes entirely through its skin.

Reptile skin is dry and covered with scutes (bony or horny external plates arising from the dermis, seen on, crocodiles, alligators and turtles) or scales as seen on lizards and snakes. Note that scutes can also be found on the feet of birds and the tails of select mammals. They are a form of armor. Lizard scales may be tubercular (nodule-like) to platelike and can even vary in different locations in the same lizard family. Snake scales add color patterns, aid locomotion and, in the rattler, can be modified to form rattles. There are no in-between rattles in the fossil record. The chameleon's skin is unique in that they can change colors to regulate heat, hide from predators and communicate.

Interestingly, even though a crocodile's hide is among the toughest and can be used for shoes, it its also among the most sensitive. Their face, is more sensitive to vibration and pressure than a person's fingertips. Many of their bumps sense faint actions along their sides.

The thorny devil lizard that lives in the deserts of Australia has a thorny, spiked, skin that is extremely hydrophobic, meaning it can readily absorb water (very important). It has ben compared to paper towels and "wicking it up". They can literally drink water through their feet.

Mammals have similar skin to ours with an epidermis on top and dermis below. Horse skin is similar, but thicker; despite that, they may actually feel pain more easily. That's because of there are more nerve endings and many are closer to the surface. Whales are notorious for thick skin. The whale shark has skin that is six inches thick and the adult sperm whale is over a foot.

Monkey skin, if evolution is correct, had to evolve from similar mammals. Lemurs are sometimes cited, but there are striking differences which include their overall size, nose size, olfactory sense, gasp strength, and scent glands. Monkeys have no scent glands.

The elasticity in our skin is readily apparent in children as they grow (spread out0, in pregnant women and in obese individuals, but this function is constantly working—every time you take in a breath or chew food; every step you take and every time you flex or extend a muscle. We owe this ability to elastin which is an extremely flexible protein. It envelops our body in a near-invisible network of crisscrossing fibrils and microfibrils. It is also found in blood vessels allowing them to expand as the higher pressure blood comes through and in lungs allowing them to expand to suck in air. One might ask were there blood vessels and/or skin originally that could not stretch. The answer is no.

Without skin, you couldn't take a bath (or shower), in fear of dying from electrolyte imbalance. A hot shower might send your body temp skyrocketing, possibly into seizure territory. Your muscles would absorb water and probably burst. If you sprayed yourself with perfume, it would be absorbed and probably damage your kidney. If you blushed, your mate would be staring at a face crowded with dilating, red blood vessels.

How aesthetic would we be if every time we took a step, took a jump-shot or did morning stretches, our skin did not shrink back to where it started? Many of us would have reams of folded skin hanging from our torso. What if skin weren't cleanable, we'd all be very dirty and probably not smell very good. Our fingers would be permanently stained with ink (or nicotine). If skin couldn't heal, we'd be covered with draining sores, forever? Our ears and nose would only be holes. Lips would be absent.

Living Structure Support

According to evolution, fish and land animals, including humans, have an endoskeleton, meaning the bones (the hard, supporting parts) are inside. Instead of being hard on the outside, perhaps the best protection, we are hardest on the inside. This may bring other benefits, such as improved flexibility, but it cannot compare to the armor from chitin.

Fish are considered, by evolutionists, to be the first vertebrates to have bone. Their bones supposedly evolved from dermal or skin structures. There's no clear proof of this, however; it's only a guess.

Bone types were divided in time between the endoskeleton such as we have on the inside and the exoskeleton like insects and crabs have on the outside. A huge change that the evolutionists say happened smoothly. As usual there's no intermediates to speak of. For the processes to work and change Intelligent Guidance was/is required, i.e. the "God of the Gaps".

The human skeleton is made up of 206 bones. We begin with 270 at birth, but many fuse. They are divided into appendicular and axial. The appendicular skeleton (126 bones) is the pelvis, the shoulders and these include the lower and upper limb bones, respectively, and the axial skeleton (80 bones)which includes the vertebral column, the rib cage, skull and associated bones.

Our bones begin as cartilaginous images (essentially templates) in the embryo. Osteoblast cells (the builders) secrete and help shape a material called osteoid, which is a gelatinous material that includes organic glue. This attracts inorganic compounds such as calcium. Other, much rarer cells called osteoclasts are part of the building and modeling process. This process is called ossification.

As the fetus grows and later as the baby grows, most of the cartilage cells die out and are replaced by bones as we know them. How both femurs grow in near-perfect unison and with near perfect symmetry is unknown. Arm and leg bones (front paws and back paws) match their counterparts. Femurs are always in the legs; the ulnas are always in the arms.

Our bones are most dense around the age of twenty-five, corresponding to, and not by accident, the years when people are the most physically active. Female skeletons tend to be smaller than male skeletons yet their pelvis is constructed differently to allow for childbirth. Unlike most primates, males do not have a penile bone. Why it dropped off, entirely, if evolution is responsible, is an enigma.

Chimpanzee skeletons are bent forward with shorter legs and longer arms (presumably to touch the ground for knuckle walking). They have smaller skulls for a smaller brain, somewhat different shaped skulls, and much sharper teeth.

Experts say that bone is much stronger than steel, on a per weight basis. If our bones were as dense as steel, we'd be incredibly strong, but unable to run and jump. Maybe never get out of bed. **Our bones are made from calcium phosphate whereas invertebrates (non-mammals) are made of calcium carbonate. How did that change? This is another evolutionary puzzle.**

There is no apparent evolutionary benefit, having the two pipelines of nerves that switch sides high in the spine. The right brain controls the left side and the left brain controls the right side of the body as if braided. And, if it's purely an 180° twist of a species body, why is it that the optic nerves to the eyes split in half and only fifty percent switch sides. That couldn't happen with a full body 180° twist. Or, select tracts of nerves change sides throughout the course of the spinal cord? There is no obvious evolutionary benefit.

MORE OF MY QUESTIONS

XII

The Inner Parts

No question we could not exist without having a heart and lungs. According to the theory of evolution, these organs came about through slow successive changes over millions of years. That is, millions to billions of very specific, interconnected changes happened in some logical order over millions of years. Note that the heart and lungs had to have evolved in complimentary ways, sharing major blood vessels and anatomically fitted..

Robots, in contrast, have no need for either organ. Oxygen might even be damaging to some. There are no waste products per se, not as humans know them. Machines merely need a renewable power source and a little lubrication. Instead of arteries, veins and capillaries, they make use of complex wiring systems. If one wanted to make a humanoid that could pass for a real person, there might be a need to invent some form of pulsing in wrist and neck arteries, suggesting there's a presence of a heart.

Microorganisms primarily depend on diffusion to get their nutrients and eliminate waste products. A host of different circulatory systems can be found throughout the invertebrate species. The earthworm has five pairs of muscular hearts (or aortic arches) that pump their blood. Insects have a single chamber heart that pumps blood to the periphery (body edges) where the respiratory system exchanges carbon dioxide for oxygen. The octopus has three hearts.

One large one to pump blood to the body and one at each gill, for a total of three, to collect oxygen and eliminate carbon dioxide from the surrounding water. In contrast to humans who have red blood caused by the effect of oxygen on hemoglobin, these animals have blue blood. Their hemoglobin is a different protein called hemocyanin. There are no signs of intermediate species with incomplete systems found in the fossil record.

Blood in insects is called hemolymph which is mostly water that bathes the body in nutrients. It can be a yellowish color, but is often clear. The red that one sees when a bug is crushed is often the pigments from their eyes.

The circulation of a fish basically relies on two chambers (we have four chambers) that receive the venous, meaning blood without oxygen which is pumped to gills to absorb oxygen replacements. From there the blood goes out to the entire body and then loops back to the heart. Sharks have a different version, basically having three chambers, but still gills.

Frogs, like many amphibians, have three chambers, i.e., two atria and one ventricle. This is the type of heart that is thought to have evolved into the mammal's four chamber organ. Blood sent to the body is a mix of low oxygen and high oxygen. The turtle has a partial septum (wall) in that ventricle leading to more oxygenated blood being sent to the body. Mammals and bird have a completed septum which results in four chambers.

The primate and whale heart look and function very similar to humans, yet the latter can be as large as a VW Beetle car with an aorta that is large enough for a person to swim through. There may be subtle genetic difference yet to be determined.

The signs of the human heart become evident at three weeks following conception and can be seen pumping blood by the fourth week. Mom's circulation and the placenta take care of nutrition, oxygen and minerals until the moment of delivery.

The human heart is an incredibly complex, multi-functional, and life-sustaining organ. It is protected by armor, namely the sternum and ribs that are flexible enough to allow breathing. It seems as if "Nature" got it right the first time through. Of course, it had to. There are no small, step-by-step, useless, partial hearts found in our distant ancestors in the fossil record. **This organ reflects clear Foresight, Purpose, Engineering, and the convergence of many, convoluted designs.**

Bruneau[48] showed that the transcription factor Tbx5 has a lot to do with heart development during the early embryological period. Cold blooded animals seem to have this factor throughout their heart, whereas warm blooded animals only have it on the left side. This, they feel, leads to the separation of the two ventricles.

Realtors say: "Location is location is location." And, so it goes with our heart. It has to be centrally located and relatively close to the brain, able to pump at least 60 times per minute x 60 minutes/hour x 24 hours/day x 365 days/year x >70 years/average lifetime. There's no time off for holidays. No rest days. It has back up systems: four separate and distinct electric systems in a line. If the main pacemaker is damaged, a second electrical system, downstream kicks in. If that is damaged, there's yet another system that can keep a person alive. The heart has to be able to repair and regenerate itself on the run. No turning the motor off and leaving it at the shop for repairs.

Our heart is actually two side-by-side pumping stations (blue or venous side and red or the arterial side). They share a common wall along with some of the plumbing and electrical systems. The blue pumping station or right side receives blue blood, which is low on oxygen from the body, and sends it on to the lungs for oxygenation. The red pump or left side receives red blood (meaning saturated with oxygen) back from the lungs and pumps it back out to every microscopic corner of the body.

---

48 Benoit Bruneau of the Gladstone Institute of Cardiovascular Disease September 3 Nature Gladstone Institutes. *"First Genetic Link Between Reptile And Human Heart Evolution Found."* ScienceDaily. ScienceDaily, 3 September 2009. <www.sciencedaily.com/releases/2009/09/090902133629.hal

Every cell has a myriad of receiving and shipping docks along the cylindrical capillary walls. Enlarge this image up to factory size. There are specific trucks (carriers) for each type of item dropped off. The sugar transport vehicle might be a long and triangular to fit into a triangular receiving dock. Oxygen comes in a giant donut-like red cell and sodium or potassium might be a geometric shape. Of course, these ports are much more complicate. Couriers (trucks, cars, vans, motorcycles bikes) more resemble twisted skeins of wool that wind, unwind and hook up in very specific ways.

Red blood cells are one of the dominant travelers through the circulatory system, but mixed in are billions of white cells looking for signs of infection or cancer. Subsets of white cells are always on a seek-and-kill mission for bacteria, viruses, and fungi invaders. There are billions of clotting factors floating around, ready to shed their cloaks and pounce. That is, upon a signal, change from inactive to active. **Mind you, how difficult life would be if clotting factors were constantly active.**

Trillions of items of all shapes, sizes, electrical charges, and complexities circulate at the same time, yet every item in the bloodstream moves along smoothly. Everything has a specific purpose, a clearcut destination and a means to connect with a complimentary dock. How cells pick off their needs from this slurry is not fully understood.

This is incredibly complex, yet organized highways, sans road rage. That is 60,000 miles of highways, avenues, streets, driveways and alleyways. Without a God of the Gaps evolution cannot explain how this all came about.

The Lungs Piece

We live in an invisible sea that is mostly oxygen, carbon dioxide, water vapor and nitrogen. Our gills are lungs. Without the presence of oxygen, we could not exist. Our pulmonary (lung) waste product is carbon dioxide. Plants have the reverse cycle, producing oxygen. This is a near-perfect, self-replenishing, life-sustaining exchange system.

Microscopic organisms breathe in many diverse ways, called cellular respiration. Many absorb oxygen through their exterior surfaces, but there is another huge group, called anaerobes, that prefer to live where oxygen is rare or absent. The latter may have been the first microscopic organisms since oxygen was likely sparse, if not absent, 4.5 billon years ago.

Some species, like sponges and jellyfish, absorb oxygen through their exterior surfaces. Fish "showed" up with gills, typically located a little behind the eyes, covered by an operculum. They extract oxygen from water after it passes through the mouth. There's no evidence of gills changing into lungs or intermediate steps anywhere in the fossil record. It's a rather big step to assume. Lungs merely appeared with massive genetic changes. Evolutionists assume there were transitional phases, but there are none.

The possible exceptions are air sacks in the lung fish, but they are just that—bags of air that inflate and deflate easily like a balloon. Their anatomy is not even close to that of lungs. Usually there are two, attached to the gastrointestinal tract, but there can be one. Fish, like the lung fish, that have these, gulp in air to fill a swim bladder which is mostly used for buoyancy. They do a reverse gulp to empty it (burp?). No animal seems to have both lungs and a swim bladder. **This is a huge evolutionary gap.**

Amphibians go about getting oxygen in similar and different ways. Tadpoles arrive with gills which they lose as they mature. They develop lungs at the same time. Different salamander species have three overlapping options for breathing: through both gills and lungs, lungs alone and/or through their skin.

Birds inhale oxygen and exhale carbon dioxide through their nostrils and mouth much as we do, but they have a series of air sacs attached to their lungs. These sacs extend into hollow bones. This makes flying easier and they use the air to help regulate their temperature as well. Convergence of design.

Whale lungs are similar in function to ours, but the air enters through a blow hole. Notably their lungs are strikingly larger than ours. The humpback whale's lungs have a total capacity of 5000 liters or about the size of a car. Our lungs have a total capacity of 6 liters or less, which is the size of two headrests in a car.

Blowholes are the whale's nostrils. They can batten down with the help of a nasal plug as water pressure increase. Some whales have only one blowhole like dolphins. Air sacs in that area help with communication sounds and echolocation. Spout shapes vary in size and shape among different types of whales and some can even be identified just by those parameters. They say the blowhole evolved from the nostrils of preceding mammals moving backwards to the top of the head, but there are no in-between nostrils. No animal or fossil to date has been shown to have blowholes that migrate from a front position topside or the back of the head.

With breathing, humans and monkeys are fairly similar. They do, however, differ in the number of lobes, the number of generations of different types of airways, in artery structure and the number and size of alveoli. Following birth, monkey lungs increase in size only while human lungs increase in size and increase the number of alveoli.

In humans the lungs start developing very early in the embryo as an out-pouching in the foregut. Throughout the nine months of gestation, it matures while submerged in amniotic fluid. It remains dormant in regard to function as it is bathed in fluid (not exposed to air). Large blood vessels that normally carry oxygen away are temporarily detoured as the placenta provides the oxygen. Being a land animal, we had to have had an automatic mechanism that could inhale specific volumes of air, extract oxygen at the innermost, deepest cellular levels of the lungs, and then transfer it to the bloodstream. Minute blood vessels (capillaries) service every cell, like the back alleys in every city block, for deliveries and pick-ups. The anatomy and cytology between chimp and man is virtually indistinguishable.

This organ reflects clear foresight, purpose, engineering, and convergence of designs. We inhale air at a rate of 12-16 times/minute, through our nostrils, where it is quickly filtered by hairs, hydrated and warmed. The air travels down (is sucked in) through the trachea (windpipe)and bronchioles of decreasing diameter, powered mostly by the diaphragm, a large muscle pushing air out and pulling it in. Ultimately, the air reaches microscopic sacs called alveoli where oxygen is exchanged for carbon dioxide. To better envision this anatomy, imagine an inverted giant, bushy broccoli stalk. Those tiny florets at the tips are the alveolar system. Microscopic monitors found in the walls of certain blood vessels can sense if our oxygen level drops too low or our carbon dioxide level goes too high. If a change is needed, they signal the diaphragm and chest muscles to take in faster/more or slower/fewer breaths until rectified.

"He had sunglasses on and I couldn't see his soul."

RABBI YISROEL GOLDSTEIN, JUST BEFORE HE WAS SHOT AT
CHABAD SYNAGOGUE IN POWAY, CALIFORNIA, APRIL 2019

XIII

The Thinking Piece

Determining whether we are the consequences of evolution or Intelligent Design may come down to deciding how consciousness and thinking came about.

The number of steps for pre-thinking organisms to eventually evolve into a multi-trillion cell, human beings, who can think, would be astronomical. Plus, every step in between would have to be useful. Not be dead ends or frayed wires. In a sense, we are all information systems. Adding the letter A to a blank/empty keyboard accomplishes nothing unless there's foresight to eventually make this a complete typewriter or computer. Adding a mutation damages the A; it doesn't improve things. Changing the monkey keyboard into a human keyboard would be mammoth.

If Intelligent Design is responsible for our ability to think, a significant portion of the process must have appeared in its entirety. **We know that organisms cannot add DNA (information) on their own, meaning more brain cells without materials and instructions.** Something, somehow delivered our tv set, unpacked it, plugged it in and even turned it on. All thinking parts had to be present at the same time, placed in the right order, functioning in the right way, and located in the right spot. To think (function) best, they must also be ready to experiment, learn and interact with other thinkers.

Using a computer keyboard again might make these points more clear. There is little purpose in having a laptop that can only type a question mark, an exclamation mark and the letter S (all steps). Add a T (a new step)—not much help. Add a P (another step)—again, not much help. But, when you add in an O, there's a little help. You might be able to type (meaning think): STOP, POTS, TOPS, POST, POT, TOP, TO, OPTS, OPT or SOP. This time use the exclamation point or the question mark, rearrange the letters, and you get meaningful information, such as: STOP POST! and STOP!! You cannot quite write a poem, a book or an encyclopedia with these, however.

If you have all the keys in place, the combinations for useful information is enormous. If the keyboard arrived with all keys functioning, connected to a computer with a screen, plugged in and turned on, you get Intelligent Design. If later, the black and white system was changed to color or your 16-inch screen was replaced by a 24-inch screen, you have Intelligent Guidance.

Birds cannot have partial wings and fly; cheetahs cannot run with partial legs. Caterpillars cannot change to butterflies using partial cocoons. **Man could never function without the keys (parts of genes) in the right place, at the right time and working in the right order.** To demonstrate this, imagine switching the keys around on your keyboard (move every key one space) and see if your typing (thinking) makes any sense.

Is our ability to think a consequence of algorithms only or something metaphysical? Or, perhaps a mix?

If thinking is truly intangible, that virtually eliminates evolution as an explanation. It's not like the tangible bone marrow making red blood cells or lymph nodes making antibodies. One cannot conjure up how items such as creativity, curiosity, empathy, complex language, joking and deductive reasoning could have slowly evolved by piecemeal through unicellular organisms, multicellular organisms, fish, amphibians, and mammals. Try writing a meaningful sentence, one word every 1000 years: "Get", "Get me", "Please get me", "Please get my a", Please get me a cup of", "Please get me a cup of coffee."

During evolution the brains of the newest species would have needed to add uncountable, genetic algorithms, on their own, through the millennia to eventually give us the ability to read and understand simple sentences. If earlier species could not think, they had to have evolved brain cells to think. That says add on. And, that strongly suggests an inherent Plan.

Merriam Webster Dictionary defines thinking as the act of using one's mind to produce thoughts, a mental activity. But, what then is mental activity? This is quite difficult to pin down. Evidence of thought among has not been found. It cannot be fossilized, mummified or precipitated. There's nothing there to carbon date. Thoughts cannot be pried from sedimentary rock, found in sedimentary layers that have been dusted off, squeezed from a plant or viewed under a microscope. It cannot be handled in any way. It can be molded, but not in a physical way. Even though one's mind is consciously aware of one's own thoughts, the actual process of how we create and hear those thoughts remains a mystery.

Try explaining thought to an extraterrestrial is somewhat like nailing Jello® to a wall. One cannot get a good handle on it. We all know what thought is when we hear it and we all can produce any number of thoughts. And those thoughts often produce more thoughts. We can edit the thought, rephrase and edit it again, twist it, taint it, without picking up any writing device. We can make it humorous or scary. But, what's really going on? Is it something metaphysical or just combinations of sophisticated algorithms working in parallel that make thinking seem extraordinary?

And, who's talking to whom inside you? Who's arguing with whom (or with what)? For example: I told myself it's best be quiet. The talking person told the same talking person to shut up? Rush Limbaugh, an American talk show host, once said on Fox: "That's one of the best questions I've ever asked myself." If there's only one person (meaning just you) inside there, why do we feel there's two having a conversation? Or, even a group debate? Plato[49] once said Thinking [is] the talking of the soul with itself.

We all speak to ourselves, of course, but why? Ray Kurzweil[50], has said that he has studied the brain for over fifty years, has the same question as I do, and was once quoted: "Just how many conscious minds do we have in our brain? There is evidence that suggests there may be more than one." Are we all split personalities? Two separate individuals melded somehow?

For purposes of my discussion, I've divided thinking into five major components: language, memory, awareness of self, awareness that others also have a functioning mind (a.k.a the Theory of the Mind or ToM), and making sense of the world around us. Subsets or tools for thinking include planning, imagining, judging, moralizing, anticipating, memorizing, sympathizing, mourning, disbelieving, recalling, reasoning, deducting, considering, calculating, regret-ting, analyzing, monitoring, criticizing, minimizing, wishing, play-ing, deceiving, predicting, reflecting, conceptualizing, categorizing, debating, self-castigating, praying, composing music, and making decisions. This list contains highlights only.

Select animals do some of these. There is specific evidence show-ing that some species can plan, anticipate, recall, mourn, empathize, and play. When an animal finds itself in an unusual situation, it can respond in an apparent thoughtful, yet unexpected way. Crows can retrieve food in unique, convoluted ways. Apes can put sign language words together in unexpected, yet meaningful, ways. This must be thinking., the sort of I know when I see it, right?

---

49 Plato was an Athenian philosopher in Ancient Greece, who founded the Plato school of thought, the first institution of higher learning in the Western world.

50 Contemporary author,, inventor and recipient of the 1999 National Medal of Honor from the White House.

One cannot communicate with another unless the first person assumes/knows that the second person can think in virtually the same manner. What good is it if you tell your housekeeper that you need the couch dusted and the person actually spreads a load of dust over the furniture[51]. Does killing two birds with one stone actually mean killing two birds? Or, does his elevator isn't stopping at the top floor mean there's an inner elevator?

I find it noteworthy that we hear the same sound waves as we speak. And, the decibel levels. There's no evidence to the contrary. An accident? It's also noteworthy that we are able to learn other languages. Is that capability in our brains an accident or Planned? Just the idea that we arrive without language skills and we are able to learn to speak, I find amazing.

Language need not be verbal. It can be any combination of written words, pictures, emojis, acronyms, codes, signing, body language, music, gestures, colors, songs, art, various animal sounds(barks, growls, chirps), splashes, touches, displays, echoes, radio signals, hissing, ultrasound, vibrations at ELF (extremely low frequencies), light signals, bioluminescence, flag signals, urine on a tree, facial expressions, ear positions, drum beats, courtship displays, scent markings, hormone scents, seismic like beating on the ground, alarm pheromones, and various dance moves like the waggle done by honeybees, the hula, a marking with skull and crossbones, or a striptease. There's no purpose in sending color signals if the recipient can only receive and interpret audio signals. Or, beating on the ground, when the recipient lives in trees. The sender and the receiver have to be on the same page. Many animals are colorblind. Signals must match reception. Complex thinking is required to understand the message(s).

A person's subjective experiences lingers in the realm of qualia. This means what you were feeling when you were listening to pleasing music,

---

51 Amelia bedelia-isms are the literal interpretations, and therefore the misunderstanding, of what has been said such as please dust the couch doesn't mean put dust on the couch. Throw the cat out doesn't mean put it in the garbage.

the feeling when your first lover kissed you, when you saw an animal suffering, when you were watching your child frolic with a puppy, and/or when you mourned the loss of a loved one. American Philosopher Daniel Dennett[52] says qualia is simply the way things seem to us. It's an unfamiliar term for virtually everything familiar to everyone one of us.

Dennett cites the feeling one gets while watching a beautiful sunset or the taste of a fine red wine as an example of qualia. I would add trying to tell an extraterrestrial from Andromeda what you feel when they might have six sunsets every day and seven on Sunday. Or, perhaps, someone who is blind from birth. Describe what the color red looks like without comparisons. Try telling that Andromedian what an orange or a pizza tastes like, when that individual has never tasted any our food, or what petting a dog feels like (if they don't have any furry animals one their planet).

Many famous philosophers and religious leaders throughout the ages have tried to explain how we think. Even, why we think. None, in my opinion, have succeeded. The reason is simple: it cannot be done. Maybe it's just a matter of technology yet to come.

With the advent of computers, some scientists are saying they will eventually reproduce consciousness and thinking. It's just a matter of time. Ray Kurzweil has said: "The essential thing is to recognize that consciousness is a biological process like digestion, lactation, photosynthesis, or mitosis." This means it is or will be measurable and reproducible by man.

Consciousness

Thinking and consciousness are tightly interwoven and nearly inseparable. Wikipedia[53] defines consciousness "as the state or quality

---

52 Properties of qualia include indescribable, unanalyzable, lacking interpersonal comparisons and unmediated.
https://dophilosophy.wordpress.com/2009/09/09/quining-qualia-daniel-dennett
53 https://en.wikipedia.org/wiki/Consciousness

of awareness or of being aware of an external object or something within oneself." This includes qualia, sentience, wakefulness, sensations, past experiences, and emotions. In 1690, John Locke[54] defined consciousness as "the perception of what passes in a man's own mind". So thinking must be the action of the mind and consciousness must be observing the mind at work. To know you're conscious is to think. It's sort of like a working artist looking at his/her own painting.

There may be two or more variations of consciousness. **To whom are you speaking when you are speaking to yourself?** Could these two entities be body & spirit? Or good & evil? Like the discussions once seen between Jiminy Cricket and Lampwick, standing on o's shoulders, in the movie Pinocchio. One voice might say: "Go ahead steal that candy. Nobody is looking." while a different voice might say: "Don't! You'll be arrested."

And, then there's the nineteenth century legend of Edward Mordrake who committed suicide at age 23. He was born with two faces, one in front that seemed normal and one in back that could not see, eat or speak out loud, but it would sneer whenever Mordrake was happy and smile whenever he was sad. He begged doctors to remove the extra face, but the surgical task was way beyond technologies. If the legend is true, he must have been victim to a partial conjoined twin ("Siamese twin"), but it makes one wonder about origins of our internal voices. Are we all a form of cerebrally-conjoined twins?

When we talk to ourselves, we can "hear" (recruit) other people's voices, including the voices of deceased friends and relatives. They can sound exactly as they once did. Both my grandmother and grandfather do so in my mind. Might this be some kind of an internal seance? Silent talkers within can sing, shout, and whisper. There can be a committee of voices. Try imagining the Beatles, a

54 Locke, John. "An Essay Concerning Human Understanding (Chapter XXVII)". Australia: University of Adelaide, 1689.

philharmonic, or a TV news team. I can conjure up a number of celebrities. Even make them do or say whatever my fancy. It can get weird.

Maybe these inner voices are Sigmund Freud's theoretic superego, ego and id? The famous 1900s psychiatrist felt the unconscious mind governs a large part of one's behavior. The id is the uncoordinated, instinctual voice (the "animal" or the untamed "child" within us). The superego is the more critical and moralizing part(the teacher, our clergy, a parental voice). The ego (the "real" you) mediates the two and being the most reasonable, tends to run the show. All of these are molded by early childhood experiences, which according to Dr. Freud, are psychosexual experiences. The lack of balance lends itself to mental illness and, sometimes, criminal behavior.

An outstanding question is whether true human thinking can be replicated by man in his quest to create artificial intelligence? This is an ongoing debate among international scientists, philosophers and clergy. If we are "simply" biological machines "who think that we think" (soulless and not Created by God), the answer is a qualified yes, but it might take many decades, maybe centuries, to find out. The task is far from simple. If there's a God-given spirit that brings us to life, guides our years and leaves us when the body dies, the answer is an unequivocal no. Either answer cannot be conclusively proven at this time.

Ancient Judaism teaches us that the body and soul are indivisible partners. One is earthy (definable); the other is spiritual (not definable). The physical components of the brain deal more with earthly things while the soul, the subjective component, deal with the spiritual aspects. The origin of this spirit, according to the Bible comes from God having blown the "breath of life" into man[55].

---

55 (Genesis 2:7).

We all have internal conversations. Sometimes that includes talking out loud. When it's silent talk, our vocal cords don't move. Accompanying sounds might be an ah-ha, a chuckle or a hmmm. **This must mean "you" are listening to you.**

Non-verbal language can also accompany silent talking. Take a glare ("with daggers"), a finger gesture, a smile, the tongue stuck out, a grin, a slammed fist or tears. Unfortunately, those who suffer from schizophrenia, lack the filters and hear many voices, some of which leads them to great harm. I've treated many schizophrenics and I specifically recall one who would repeatedly stop his medications and return to a spot under a bridge to worship a god of the river. He would go without food and water for days.

Inner thoughts cannot be heard even if one were to put a stethoscope over a person's vocal cords. They do not move. We do know, however, the brain displays different electrical wave patterns in very specific areas depending on what is being said, sensed and/or imagined. If it comes from the realm of vision, the electrical changes happen in the occipital lobes of the brain. If it's hearing, it's the temporal lobes. These waves come in distinct patterns as well. Gamma waves have a lot to do with information processing and memory. Beta waves have more to do with conscious thought and problem solving. And, theta waves have a lot to do with sleep, relaxation and intuition. These can be mixed together, overlap and occur in different ratios. If flat, of course, the individual has passed. Well, not always. Children who fall into frozen ponds may seem deceased to first responders by all measures, but ER doctors don't call them dead until they are warm and then found to be dead. Some miraculously come back.

In 2012, Physicist Stephen Hawking, who was paralyzed by the progressive disease amyotrophic lateral sclerosis (ALS or Lou Gehrig's disease), was fitted with an iBrain[56] inside a headband in an

---

56 https://newatlas.com/ibrain-stephen-hawking-communicate-brainwaves/23182/

effort to convert his thoughts to words. The device was the product of neuroscientist Philip Low's work and did show changes in wave activity with different activities such as watching tv and sleeping. The wave patterns could not be converted to words, however.

Yet.

The science of brain-to-text, like speech-to-text computers, is evolving wherein machines convert a person's brain waves into text. That is simply typing with your thoughts by using electrodes placed on the brain. Peter Brunner[57] and others were able to convert electrical patterns to words while the subject was reading such texts as JFK's inaugural speech or Humpty Dumpty. These electrodes had to be on or in the brain, however not on the scalp, This invasive procedure limited volunteers to seizure patients with electrodes already in place. Accuracy ranged from 25-50%. For obvious safety and ethical reasons, electrodes could not be placed inside the heads of normal volunteers. Yet, there may come a day when a malevolent dictator may impose this technology on captured enemies of the state—even if it requires drilling holes in the prisoner's skull. That said, the advancement would be terrific for patients paralyzed with ALS and certain strokes.

The ability to read a person's thoughts by having computers translate will surely come. They can already convert select sentences from inner thoughts to written words with brain implants[58]. The internet says DARPA is working on using a soldier's EEG (electrical brain tracings) to silently communicate with other soldiers on the battlefield. How might that look if a future, government agency could capture all of your thoughts? The Chinese, using the newest artificial intelligence, can monitor students's moods with computers by evaluating facial expressions. They can detect anger, fear, disgust,

57 Her C, Heger D, dePesters, A, et al. "Brain-to-Text: Decoding Spoken Sentences From Phone Representations in the Brain," Front. Neurosci. 2015.
58 G.K. Anumanchipalli, J. Chartier and E.F. Chang. "Speech Synthesis From Neural Decoding of Spoken Sentences,"*Nature*. Vol. 568, April 25, 2019, p. 493. doi:10.1038/s41586-019-1119-1

surprise, happiness and sadness. This began with simple facial recognition of students entering the school building.

A future telling event is the use of brain waves and neurons, in particular, to move a robotic arm. In 2013, Erik Sorto, a quadriplegic, had electrodes inserted in his brain. This work was done by Richard Anderson at Caltech. Soon, Sorto could read and control some of these electrical waves just by the intention to move. He had been asked what he would like to achieve at the initiation of the trial. His response was to hold a cup of beer and drink it. Indeed, at one year, after learning to raise and twist the arm, grip and shake hands, he accomplished his goal. Noted this was only the motor component. Sensing the grip may follow someday.

Concerning The Evolution Of Thinking

It's apparent that you are capable of thinking if you are reading this book. Thinking is a wonderful process that helps define and guide us. Imagine life without it. We might be slinking through woods, naked, fighting off other predators for scraps of food, sleeping high in trees and dying from the smallest of infections such as an animal bite or a puncture wound in the foot.

Thinking helps make life worthwhile. It can give us enormous pleasure and hope for the future. It gives us thoughts to live by, words to say and plans to follow, but it can also give us terrible pain and lead us astray. Are we unique in the animal world? The answer, of course, is yes, but maybe not as unique as we'd like to believe. Did our thinking, like a typewriter, start with a few typewriter keys or amino acids in the primordial pool? Or, did it start with the first fertilized human egg. Then, as it gained letters, it gained thinking skills, through the millennia just like gills to lungs and quadrupedal walking to bipedal walking?

One might think that brain tissue would have diminished in size and thereby capability over the eons due to mutations (damage) from injuries and cosmic rays, not add on new, information-gathering and assessing matter. No one knows how new genetic capabilities (DNA) is added. Instead, humans have the largest brains (compared to body size) of all living beasts and arguably the most complex. It's not size or ratio, alone, however, that supports the most sentient creatures. Some dinosaurs appear to have had huge brains, based on the size of the cavities found inside fossilized skulls. Some think T. Rex may have been extremely smart, gifted with incredible sight, smelling and hearing[59].

One might think that increased brain size may mean increased intelligence (and thinking) in the animal world. Note that the elephant and the whale are quite smart, but size isn't the only factor. Some of an animal's IQ has to do with how the parts are connected, how many parts are connected to each other, and how dense the cells are. The octopus is an exception to all land-based, thinking animals. How'd that happen? Dropped from the heavens like a tropical fish added to an aquarium?

The encephalization quotient (EQ)[60] is sometimes used to measure brain size per body size. The average EQ for mammals is 1.0. The higher the number, the smarter the animal. For example, the average dog measures at 1.2, the elephant at 2.0, chimps at 1.2, the bottlenose dolphin at 4 and humans at 7. Noted, the Troodon, a bird-like, four-foot tall dinosaur, had an EQ over 7.0. Some scientists have speculated that if the species had not been wiped out by the K/T extinction 66 million years ago we would have very intelligent reptoids. These are imagined animals with the physique of men walking on two legs, a small tail and a human shaped skull and face, yet their skin is reptilian and their hands are three fingered claws. Some say the more aggressive citizens of the world have retained some of that reptilian mindset.

---

59 https://www.pressreader.com/uk/focus-science-and-technology/20180613/281509341868801

60 Berns, Gregory, *What's It Like to Be a Dog And Other Adventures in Animal Neuroscience* (Basic Books 2017) 63.

Many questions linger, such as how did the brain continue to develop, improve, enlarge (especially the cortex) and change through evolution and eventually become a major guiding force for each of us? How did it "know" to do that? Did natural selection set us up to play video games and fly to the moon?

One might wonder what the first glimmer of thought actually looked like. Did an accidental, microscopic ball of specialized nerve cells conjure up something? Maybe it contained a whole slew of blueprints, many pre-set to make further blueprints in the next generations, and these were also pre-set to make additional blueprints down the millennial road. Like an Olympic relay race and passing to sophisticated computer rather than a baton. Very hard to buy.

Too Many Steps

Darwinists speculate that lightning struck a primordial soup billions of years ago and that set forth a complex series of events that eventually lead to people with thinking brains? Carl Sagan once told me, in a personal conversation, that evolution from one-celled organisms into a seventy-five trillion cell organism like ourselves would be easy in the few billion years life has existed. He shrugged his shoulders, as if it were a no-brainer, and added, "Easily."

I disagreed then and I disagree now, even more.

The first amino acids in this electrified soup could not think, move about, or plan a future. Or, so we think. Did that lightning strike give these floating chemicals a way to reproduce? There's no way to know with certainty, but we don't find random, organic products reproducing themselves nowadays. If not destroyed by the burn(the likely scenario), these new "pre-living" chemicals probably became chemical bumper cars, randomly floating about, occasionally bumping into each other to no avail until the soup dried up and the dust blew away.

But, suppose I'm wrong. Living entities did come about, perhaps looking like algae. Where did future capabilities to change (and improve) come from? There is no proof chromosomes can add DNA (blueprints) on their own. Millennia later, these living beings formed plants and animals. Later, they formed us. All by accident? All without a plan?

To eventually evolve the human brain, many trillions(+) of different additions and changes would have had to happen to create to that first organism, in parallel ways, in the right order, at the right time. Note there are approximately 1.5 million known species on Earth and many more yet to be found, particularly in the deep seas and the microscopic world. Every species seems to have a variation on the brain, a control center, the place where the blueprints are stored, studied and copied. Discussions of theory of evolution cannot (as yet) account for our capacity to think; and so, supporters tend to avoid the subject or simply treat it lightly.

A supporter of Intelligent Design might ask a Darwinist how thinking and consciousness came about and kept improving. In many ways, that possibility runs counter to the Second Law of Thermodynamics[61]. Improving virtually anything in Nature requires work and energy from the outside, not serendipity and happenstance. Things normally rust, rot, dissolve, shred, collapse, fade and/or disintegrate over time if left on their own. Not get bigger, better, tougher, more complicated. An animal runs faster because that capability is already in their genes(tool box). A mutation might hobble the same animal.

As the brain evolved to our level, the vocal cords had to move downward, change and improve for use. What was the driving force to do that? Foresight that the next species will need to talk? Language eventually came about, but it had to follow the appropriate brain cells (for thinking, speaking, seeing, and hearing, etc). One might joke about which word was uttered first. My guess is early profanity, but, it might have been "me (name)" pointing at oneself and "you, (name)".

---

61 https://en.wikipedia.org/wiki/Second_law_of_thermodynamics

Might there be a middle ground between evolution and Intelligent Design, such as Intelligent Guidance of evolutionary processes? Might that be called the Theory of Accidentally on Purpose? The gaps between species, such as those documented between fish and amphibian, amphibian and reptile, and monkey and man, were aided by or manipulated by an unconfirmed intelligence. This, some feel, might explain how so many useless (on their own) steps could have happened in a serial fashion, thereby changing one species into another. An artist can easily show this and words in texts can express it, but genetics alone actually cannot. The task is insurmountable.

The derivation of an intangible such as thought is hard to study, let alone prove. One cannot say with absolute certainty that dinosaurs did or didn't think. We might (correctly?)assume that dinosaurs pondered where and how to get their next meal, how to protect their young, and how to avoid becoming another animal's dinner. Try to test my hypothesis. Even if they were still among us, who would put the dab of color on a T. Rex's forehead?

To fortify the Darwinist explanation for evolution and thought, one must show that ancient species actually could think. Of course, we camot go back to administer IQ tests to dinosaurs. And, verbal tests are obviously not doable with ancient beasts such as crocodiles and coelacanth fish. The best we can do is check contemporary species and see if there's a steady improvement in the processes of thinking as one climbs the tree of life. This, with some exceptions like the octopus, we find is true. Is it proof? No.

At some point in evolution, there had to have been two separate and parallel (sex-related) pathways going through reciprocal changes (male/female). One would think they had to have interacted in comparable ways to continue (or improve side-by-side) the species. Another convergence. In the case of humans, men and women could think, could talk, and physically interact. Both had sexual feelings. We don't know exactly where the male/female split happened in evolution, if it did, and how they evolved in such compatible ways.

The Bible, of course, has its answer: God made Adam and Eve. Both complete packages. In evolution, male and female monkeys needed parallel anatomical, physiological, hormonal and emotional courses(changes) to become people. That is, perfect matches. The God of Gaps would be needed. Each modification requires billions of changes, additions and modifications. What came along that caused male hormones to increase while female hormones decreased in human males? The opposite happened in females. This cannot be explained by steps that came along every few years or so. It would not work. Like a "working" car having one or two wheels and later adding the third and, thereafter, the fourth. The typical car needs four wheels from the very start to even roll.

Who Thinks?

Modern science has documented that there are purposeful communications between microorganisms, plants, fish, reptiles amphibians and all mammals, suggesting consciousness. The 2012 Cambridge Declaration on Conscious[62] states " . . . the weight of evidence indicates that humans are not unique in possessing the neurological substrates that generate consciousness. Non-human animals, including all mammals and birds, and many other creatures, including octopuses, also possess these neurological substrates."

Some might argue that lower animals lack consciousness, with good reason. At a minimum, it's not the same as ours. Their "thinking" is more instinctual. It may only be instinctual. And, it lacks morality—we think. Consciousness and instinct are not mutually exclusive. If you were suddenly attacked by a bear, an angry dog, or some bad guy, everything you might do for the next few seconds would be instinctual. Boiled down that would be fight or flight.

---

62 In 2012, a group of neuroscientists attending a conference on "Consciousness in Human and non-Human Animals" at Cambridge University in the UK, signed *The Cambridge Declaration on Consciousness15*.

The portia spider[63] hunts web-spiders. It shows intelligent hunting behavior, which also suggests the ability to learn. They are capable of deceiving and adapting strategies before attacking. Elephants have shown signs of empathy. There's an instance[64] where a nearly blind old woman was lost and when found, elephants were guarding her. In another situation, orphaned African elephants[65] recognized their earliest caregivers years later. A study by Oakland University psychologist Jennifer Yonk[66] showed that four orangutans and one lowlands gorilla could pair up matching photos, side by side, of mammals with mammals and reptiles with reptiles. A study of corvids (the crow family) on tool manufacturing, mental time travel and social recognition suggests they think much like monkeys yet they lack a visible neocortex[67] in their brain. Chimps have been shown to make reconciliation gestures after fighting by pointing to food[68].

Do Single-Celled Animals Think?

Maybe. They are grouped as prokaryotic organisms, which are bacteria and archaea, and eukaryotes, which include single-celled fungi, single-celled algae and protozoa. Note that sperm qualify as single-celled organisms. Do they "think" when some pave the way for faster sperm, fight another man's sperm or play odd man out

63 Piper, Ross , *Extraordinary Animals: An Encyclopedia of Curious and Unusual Animals* (2007, Greenwood Press).

64 https://news.nationalgeographic.com/2015/07/150714-animal-dog-thinking-feelings-brain-science/

65 ibid https://news.nationalgeographic.com/2015/07/150714-animal-dog-thinking-feelings-brain-science/

66 https://www.scientificamerican.com/article/many-animals-can-think-abstractly/

67 Nathan J. Emery, Nicola S. Clayton,"The Mentality of Crows: Convergent Evolution of Intelligence in Corvids and Apes" *Science* 10 Dec 2004: Vol. 306, Issue 5703, pp. 1903-1907

68 https://www.elsevier.com/connect/animals-do-think-surprising-insights-into-the-evolution-of-cognition-and-communication

to decide who gets to fertilize the egg? No one knows how that is determined.

Micro-organisms, like bacteria, may not think as we envisage it, yet they communicate important and different information, in very purposeful ways, at appropriate times. They definitely show memory and a chemical language. Self-awareness or awareness of feelings in others, if even present, has not been detected. Nonetheless, there are a number of examples wherein critical information is forwarded, assimilated and acted upon.

Take quorum sensing. One example happens when an increasing large concentration of certain bacteria present in the bladder of an elderly person. Together, in some fashion, they seem to decide to initiate a full-on attack. In medical terms this is called sepsis, essentially meaning the infection spreads to the bloodstream and is having a serious impact. Somehow, this happens once bacteria numbers are reach a critical level. Like a military invasion, sheer numbers overwhelm defense measures and can often kill the host.

There must be some determination made, such as a chemical and electrical sound-off, which is followed by some a broad communication to move out, to invade. If it is eventually determined that all thinking, whenever/wherever, is really a robotic maneuver using algorithms, microorganisms must do it, too. This action, and many like it throughout Nature, is clearly deliberate, timed and coordinated.

Some bacteria also seem to know when to capture or copy genes, e.g., to create antibiotic resistance, from other organisms. Some organisms seem to know where to set up shop (start infecting), such as only infecting the gut (salmonella), the lungs (pneumococcus), the brain,(meningococcus, rabies) or the kidneys (E.coli and others). Some know when it's time to release a toxin. Obviously, this is not thinking as we imagine it, but when dealing with evolution, the earliest form of thinking may be some modulation of instincts[69]?

---

69 Meaning an innate, fixed pattern of behavior in animals in response to certain stimuli.

Amoeba and specifically amoebic dysentery and brain-eating amoeba are among the best known single cell organisms and among the most feared. Especially, the brain-eater They tend to live in warm water which can be certain lakes, hot springs, aquariums and untreated municipal water. There is purposeful movement toward food by extending their pseudopods and engulfing the prey. The brain-eating variety is attracted to a person's nose. Specifically, the chemicals that are found between nerve cells associated with the sense of smell. From there they travel to the frontal lobe of the brain which deals with thinking. Altered thinking obviously can be the first presentation.

Other microorganisms that cause red tide are in the single-celled algae that use something resembling quorum sensing or sudden group decisions. Under certain conditions they will suddenly bloom in oceans, bays and/or estuaries, forming huge areas of brown or red scum. They kill virtually every fish and most life in the area. They can be very toxic to nearby wildlife and humans.

Again, if thinking is merely ON and Off switches, this too might be the beginning of thinking for a Darwinist.

As one moves up the evolutionary tree, there is increasing evidence of purposeful actions that may actually reflect a form of thinking. Note that the tree has, through the decades, undergone many revisions and now can be found, depending on the source, to have many different looks with different numbers of branches and different types of branches. Exceptions (the inexplicables), placed to the side or ignored.

Do simple multicellular organisms think? Species like these with clumps of cells working together are said to go back at least 3 billion years. Some work together doing the same chores and others are rather independent, perhaps hanging together for protection only; and, others link together to take on different chores for the good of the whole. No one knows how some of these individual cells changed, but there may be at least forty-six separate lines. Theories of why and how abound which include saying a cell divided into two daughter cells that somehow stuck together, that a function-specific, slug-like group formed, called a grex. Lacking bones and similar structure, they are not well preserved in the fossil record. Most ideas regarding derivation are only guesses. Even viruses are blamed (given credit) for their own changes. How? The virus slips a segment into the DNA of a cell, reproduces itself a dozen fold or more, but doesn't change as far as we know.

Multicellular organisms increased in their number of participants and ultimately became fishlike. How? No Darwinist really knows. Darwin didn't address the beginning so life, possibly because his theories didn't apply.

Whether early multicellular species, a half to a whole billion years ago, could think or make decisions is mere conjecture. We believe that a sponge cannot think, yet they can show purposeful behavior under select conditions. An experiment by H. V. Wilson[70] showed sponge cells separated from parent animal will regroup and form a new, growing sponge. If two different sponge cell groups are mixed, they will find their own, group up and grow. This, according to the theory of evolution, might be the way cellular organisms progressed up the tree of life.

Individual cells and/or groups of cells can react to changes in their environment. One study[71] suggests that sponges have a rudimentary sense organ manifest by cilia and can, as a group, react to sediments in surrounding water. This causes the whole animal to contract down to expel them. It's called a "sneeze" response. Evolutionists say this is a predecessor to our sense organs. Just because it sneezes?

---

70 An experiment performed by H. V. Wilson of the University of North Carolina was published in the 1907 issue of the Journal of Experimental Zoology (Wilson 1907).

71 Ludeman, D.A., N. Farrar, A. Riesgo, J. Paps, and S.P. Leys (2014). "Evolutionary Origins of Sensation in Metazoans: Evidence for a New Sensory Organ in Sponges. " *BMC Evolutionary Biology*, 14(3). doi:10.1186/1471-2148-14-3.

Do Insects Think?

Insects occupy one of the larger branches of the evolutionary tree. They are most likely connected to crabs. They are, in some ways, comparable. Clive D. L. Wynne[72] wrote that honeybees can learn and show evidence of reasoning. He recorded: "We might almost say that bees engage in abstract thought." An example is the foraging on alfalfa flowers. In one study spring-loaded devices were used to trap a bee's tongue. Older and more experienced bees learned how extract the nectar without getting injured.

Insects have a rudimentary brain which remotely resembles the human brain, albeit much smaller and simpler. Many researchers believe they have a rudimentary consciousness. They can think about select items such as food and aspects of work. And, change their mind.

Andrew B. Barron and Colin Klein in the Proceedings of the National Academy of Sciences[73] proposed that insects have the capacity for consciousness, it may mean robots with AI can have minimal consciousness.

Insects definitely have purposeful actions which may involve some consciousness for protecting their authority, food, water and hive. Certain groups seem to show anger when aroused. Bees and the like also seem to show love to their queens. There is an obvious loyalty. The white-mustached portia spider, cited earlier, is considered, by some, to be in the top ten smartest animals on the planet. They are probably the smartest bug. They can pluck "songs" on their web that attract other spiders(their prey).

---

72 Clive D. L. Wynne , *Do Animals Think?, (Princeton University Press, 2006), 35.*
73 Andrew B. Barron and Colin Klein, "What Insects Can Tell Us About the Origins of Consciousness." PNAS May 3, 2016 113 (18) 4900-4908; published ahead of print April 18, 2016 https://doi.org/10.1073/pnas.1520084113

Do Fish Think?

Most experts think that they don't, but no one knows that with certainty and there are some suggestive studies that they might. They do have a tiny brain; so, perhaps, they have the tiniest of thoughts. All seem to know how to avoid predators, find food and locate mates. People who work on fish farms say their fish seem to know when it's feeding time, which is not entirely a natural instinct. None wore watches. Cod can be taught to pull a string for food. Sharks have a brain-to-body mass ratio similar to mammals and can learn, too. This was noted watching juvenile lemon sharks investigating novel objects[74].

Jellyfish, who are not really fish, were once thought to be incapable of thinking, just unpleasant animals floating wherever currents carried them and stinging anything and anybody that crosses their paths. Yet, there are some interesting exceptions. The most prominent might be the box jellyfish, which can swim, even dodge objects in the water in the Caribbean mangrove swamps. It doesn't have a brain, yet it has 24 eyes— four different types (upper and lower lens eyes, pit eyes and slit eyes). The upper eyes always look up and lower look down. The upper eyes actually have a lens, a cornea and retina, not so different from our eyes. If a box jellyfish is taken several meters from the mangroves, they can see well enough to swim (and will) swim back into the mangroves[75]. Testing in the lab shows they can avoid obstacles and see color. It's believed they can tell the size of objects. The presence of their eyes cannot yet be explained by evolutionists. One could easily feel their ability to assess their environment indicates some form of thinking.

---

74 Guttridge, T.L., van Dijk, S., Stamhuis, E.J., Krause, J., Gruber, S.H. and Brown, C. (2013). "Social Learning in Juvenile Lemon Sharks, Negaprion brevirostris," Animal Cognition16 (1): 55–64. doi:10.1007/s10071-012-0550-6. PMID 22933179.
75 Garm, A. M. Oskarsson, and D.-E. Nilsson. 2011. "Box Jellyfish Use Terrestrial Visual Cues for Navigation," Current Biology 21:798-803.

Do Lizards Think?

Bearded dragons can be taught to open cage doors to get food by watching a trained bearded lizard do it first. Whereas the same breed kept away from the trained lizard could not open the door. This was reported by researchers at the University of Lincoln in the UK and Hungary[76]. Researchers elsewhere report lizards can feel emotions which include fear, aggression, and pleasure when stroked or fed. Iguanas have shown a preference for certain people over others. It's not known how much they actually think, but judging by their body language some form of thought, mostly seen attracting mates and discouraging predators is probably going on. How conscious is it? That's your guess.

Do Birds Think?

The brains in birds are an evolutionary step up from reptile brains. They clearly have actions that suggest thinking, and if not our evolutionary predecessors, one might wonder how that process came about separately. The Ragsdale study[77] showed birds and mammals have similar nerve cell circuits or wiring.

Caledonian Crows can learn how to make tools and use them. When given the choice or task, they select tools that are appropriate[78], similar to monkeys and octopuses. Scrub jays will hide their food a second time if they "think" a rival has seen them burying the goods the first time. Crows have been shown to drop heavy objects in tubes of water to float food closer (within range of their beak). Crows have also been shown to use a small stick to get a larger stick to fish out a meaty snack out of a hole.

76 http://www.reptilesmagazine.com/Lizards/Information-News/Bearded-Dragon-Lizards-Are-Smarter-That-You-Might-Think/

77 J Dugas-Ford, JJ Rowell & CW Radsdale, "Cell-type Homologies and the Origins of the Neocortex." (2012) *Proc Nat Acad Sci US* 109:16974-9, *doi:10.1073/pnas.1204773109.*

78 Kenward, B, Rutz, C, Weir, A.S and Kacelnik, A (2006) "Development of Tool Use in New Caledonian Crows: Inherited Action Patterns and Social Influences, " Animal Behaviour (72), 1329-1343 .

Darwin wrote in *The Descent of Man:* "The perception, if not the enjoyment, of musical cadences and of rhythm is probably common to all animals, and no doubt depends on the common physiological nature of their nervous systems". A prime example is the video that has gone viral of a sulfur-crested cockatoo head banging, claw-stomping dance to the Backstreet Boys "Everybody".

Japanese crows will drop nuts to the street for passing cars to smash and then wait for the red light to retrieve them. Hummingbirds seem to know all the flowers in their sphere of operation, which can exceed a thousand.

The African Grey Parrot can mimic our speech, associate words and say short sentences. A Grey named Alex could name over fifty objects, seven colors, five shapes and numerical values up to six. Birds definitely can tell people apart and often show preferences. The Baya weaver bird may be the only bird, shown to date, that will die very shortly after its partner dies. An emotional collapse? This strongly suggests awareness. They literally mate for life. Birds are known for good memories and certain communications of all sorts. This too supports the idea that they can think.

Do Octopuses Think?

These characters are presumed descendants of the clam family. Looking at them, it's hard to believe that they can have a single thought, yet they make virtually everyone's top ten smartest animals' list. Sometimes, they can even be found in the top five. They are masters at camouflage and disguise plus they have short and long term memory capabilities. They have a small brain, but not a small brain function. About two-thirds of their "thinking" nerve cells can be found in their tentacles.

Scientists[79] have found that octopuses can navigate their way through mazes, solve problems quickly and remember their solutions,

79 Borell, Brendan. "Are Octopuses Smart?" Scientific American Feb 27, 2009

at least for the short term. They know when to impersonate crabs, snakes, or even poisonous fish; they can pull off any mimicry with ease. Social media has a video showing an octopus mimicking a coconut that suddenly sprouts two tiny legs and runs away. Another video shows a small octopus climbing into a clam shell, pulling it closed and rolling down an incline as if it were a ball. These animals are incredible escape artists, able to "think and see" with the tips of their tentacles. They find food inside small tunnels or holes and can escape through narrow passageways measured in advance by a tentacle tip. Their arms "think".

Play is thought to be an example of higher IQ and thinking; and, octopuses have been known to play with empty pill vials. Stories suggest they are very hard to keep in an aquarium. They constantly want to take things apart like latches and lids. Social media has a video of an octopus unscrewing the top of a jar. A well known story involves an octopus in the Brighton Aquarium 100 years ago. Every night it would leave its own aquarium and grab a fish from a nearby aquarium to eat and return before morning. They weren't smart enough to clean up the wet trail on the floor, however.

Octopuses can also build defensive structures with stones, make tools out of coconuts and shells, and rapidly change color. Some can mimic virtually any surface they are lying on, especially options found along a seafloor. An octopus in the Sea Star Aquarium in Coburg, Germany, seemed to have a sense humor. By squirting a stream of water at a spotlight, the system would short out and cause darkness, repeatedly, until an official caught on.

Do Sea Mammals think?

The late Dr. Ron Schusterman the founder of Pinniped Cognition and Sensory Systems Laboratory in Santa Cruz showed that sea lions could understand over 7000 combinations of hand signals (e.g., fetch, tail touch, flipper touch). Dr. Reichmuth who carried on his work showed these animals could do "what-if-and-then" problems with pictograms. For example, they could be taught that a picture of (what if) spiral follows a picture of (then) rectangle and (what if) spiral, (then) a circle. They knew the correct order, repeatedly. Social media has a video of a sea lions showing appreciation to divers for removing an impaled object. The animal seemed to be quite knowing.

Dolphins and whales are said to be the smartest animals in the oceans. Dolphins are often considered the second smartest animal in the world, especially the Bottlenose Dolphin. They mourn their dead, show altruism and can be empathetic. They seem to show sadness and joy; they often play with each other and humans when present. They have complex social structures, communicate with each other and seem to plan hunts. When brain size is compared to body size (EQ), they are second to man. Their cerebral cortex, where social activities, abstract thinking and communications are handled, is actually larger than that of a human's. Perhaps, they are smarter than we are.

Do non-human, land mammals think?

The answer is a likely yes. Some call this animal cognition and there are new findings that show some animals can plan, anticipate, calculate, recall, mourn, empathize, play, deceive, and/or sympathize. Another criteria, often missed by texts, will an animal, in an unusual situation, will respond in an apparent thoughtful, sometimes unnatural or unexpected way. There are many good examples of this behavior on social media. Not everything is what it seems, however, so one must beware things are faked or specifically set up. We love to train animals to mimic our actions and that thereby makes more like us.

A standout for me was a Facebook video showing one dog, helping another dog that had been struck by a train and was stuck in the middle of railroad tracks. Both were border collies. The injured dog (a she) looked alert, but obviously was hurt and unable to move. The protecting dog (a he) would not allow anyone to come close. He brought her food somehow and kept her warm as there was snow around. The animal shelter folks were notified by the train conductor.

The film shows the protecting dog lying down next to the injured dog for a scary few seconds as a train raced over them. The protecting dog seemed to be pressing the injured dog's head down. Both escaped unscathed. Eventually folks from the animal shelter were able to pull the male away and help the other. The injured dog was treated and, later on, both were adopted. Granted, this is not a scientific study, but I don't see how it could have been staged or misinterpreted. If truly an untampered incident, there's no way this could have happened without animal cognition.

There have been several instances where a family dog has sought out searchers and lead them to a lost family member. Dogs naturally will protect children (and others) from danger. Was that in their genetic wiring from the very start of mammals or added in some, thus far, unknown way, during evolution? Recall we don't have evidence that new DNA can be added, as such. Or, was it a consequence of Foresight? A part of Design?

One FEMA video, taken during the aftermath of Hurricane Katrina, shows rescuers in a boat coming upon a pug-like dog effusively barking. It repeatedly swam toward their boat and then quickly away, refusing to be caught. The dog, led them to a broken basement window where it dove inside under the water and inside. The rescuers, came in through the front door and soon found the pug with a frightened cat that was stranded on a high shelf. This is not all that unique. A number of dogs through the years have been documented leading rescuers to their injured owner(s) or other pets. A female dog will beg for food only to take it to her pups.

Many YOU-TUBEs showing heroic animals might be staged, but I believe there are some with highly suggestive proof of animal cognition. Another one that intrigued me was a black, lab-like dog standing over a partner dog who had fallen into a backyard swimming pool. Both dogs looked frantic as the dog in the pool struggled to pull itself over the edge. The first dog dove in, pushed the other dog up over the edge and then swam to the stairs to get out. It was filmed by a stationery camera, presumably home surveillance.

Many animals appear to think, demonstrated by an awareness of their environment and memory of past occurrences such as pain and pleasure. Jane Goodall[80] showed chimps have memories by selectively shunning or even repeatedly attacking a certain member when they return.

Many animals show empathy, a phenomenon which is seemingly impossible to have without thinking. A meerkat will stay behind to care for an injured or dying member of its group. Squirrels and dogs will hover over a killed partner looking as if they upset, perplexed and/or even sad. Dogs have been known to stay at a master's tombstone for years. The movie "Hachi: A Dog's Tale" with Richard Gere, exemplified this. It retells the true Japanese story of a rescued dog, its intense love for its new owner, and its extreme devotion. This is particularly evident toward the end of the film. Hachi continued waiting at the train station every night for his owner to come home even though the man had died of a heart attack years before. Just the image of this dog waiting through rain, snow and bright sunlight, day after day, season after season, still saddens me when I ponder it. Pet owners, I'm sure, would understand the feeling. And, this is not the only case of extreme devotion. Dogs will hang out or return to the deceased owner, repeatedly. Horse, too, have shown this enduring and loving devotion.

My dog must be thinking "I want some loving" every time she puts her paw on my arm to request a good scratch. Certainly, those are my thoughts. Biased? Maybe, so, but her thinking skills are readily

---

80 Goodall, J , "Social Rejection, Exclusion, and Shunning among the Gombe Chimpanzees, Journal of Ethology and Sociobiology," 1984 (7), 227-234.

evident when we play ball. If I put my hands behind my back, after faking a throw, she just stares at me waiting for the correct action. She fell for this fake only once. If I show her that right hand is empty, however her head and eyes shift to the left arm which is behind me. Dogs will also tease their masters by bringing a ball or stick back to them, lay it down just out of reach, and then grab it before the master can. They must be thinking: I fooled you. I'm sure of it :-).

The border collie is generally considered the smartest dog breed in the world, closely followed by the poodle, German shepherd, golden retriever, and Doberman pinscher. Border collies dominate many dog sports and dog dancing. Sara and Hero, a dance act, took 5th place on America's Got Talent(AGT) during the twelfth season. In 2007 researchers at Wofford College taught a border collie to recognize the names of 1022 objects, and to follow orders to fetch each one separately. These dogs can easily learn routines and virtually learn to do anything any other breed can do.

Not surprising, rats are among the smartest animals. They are commonly studied, partly due to their size, which is limited care needs, and the lack of outcry from PETA. Their physiology and psychology are similar to ours. Researchers claim they show excitement, remorse and stress. They are particularly known for their ability to solve mazes which many researchers say must require thinking.

Many parts within all animal brains are organized and structured similar to ours. So, might one easily assume that their subjective feelings are similar? Some of us like to think so. It's called anthropomorphizing; it's the act of attributing human characteristics to our pets and other animals. Some of us are certain that we have seen our dogs smile and even laugh. I'm certain I have. Many of us have seen their dog cry with the death of a loved one, man or dog. Does a dog think something when sniffing another dog's rear end? They must. Why else do it? ;-)

In the past some scientists were reluctant to believe animals could actually think. Maybe, that was anthropic arrogance. Darwin was very clear, however, that many animals have emotions. These writings, I feel, are his best. Social media is loaded with videos showing homecoming soldiers and their dogs going berserk with excitement. My two Rottweilers once knocked me to the ground with kisses and hugs when I returned from a month-long trip. It's impossible to misunderstand what's going on.

The PBS Nature episode "Animal Reunions" showed a wealthy Englishman who owns a personal rescue-zoo in England meeting up with a gorilla he had set loose in Africa five years before. The animal not only recognized him, but came out of the forest when called. He was visibly happy and affectionate. A similar circumstance happened when a researcher with Jane Goodall met up with a chimp she had rescued and raised years before. And, two elephants were obviously loving when reunited with their rescuer, Julius Latoya in Kenya. One African photographer made friends with a wild cheetah that disappeared months later. When he finally found her, she had cubs and she allowed him to play with them. That would be unheard of, actually fatal, under other circumstances.

In many cultures elephants are also viewed as animals with wisdom. They seem to have an inborn GPS system, a mental map that always leads them back to watering holes, food sites and burial grounds. They have striking self-awareness and clearly show emotions such as grief and compassion. They can use a large number of tools correctly. Suda, a four year old elephant in Thailand, can actually paint a picture of another elephant.

Chimps and apes, the experts say, are the smartest animals on Earth, short of us, of course. Darwinists say they began evolving into human-like species about 6-8 million years ago. The 2005 Genome Project[81] showed that we share 98% of their genes. That said, there

---

81 Per Wikipedia: "The Human Genome Project was an international scientific research project with the goal of determining the sequence of nucleotide base pairs that make up human DNA, and of identifying and mapping all of the genes of the human genome from both a physical and a functional standpoint. It remains the world's largest collaborative biological project. (1990-2006) "

are so many genes which are turned on or off, it's really hard to know. Plus, 2% of six billion nucleotide bases is a hefty 100 million differences. Chimps supposedly can beat college educated people on select memory exams, use computers to solve select numerical problems, and do sign language.

Language And Evolution

Language is a criteria often used to prove the presence of thinking. It must be qualified by having a recipient individual who understands the same utterances or signals. Otherwise, expressing oneself might be nonsensical utterances. Signing by chimpanzees and gorillas clearly meet these criteria. Whales definitely sing songs for different occasions and albatrosses have a very chatty mating courtship. All this qualifies as a form of language.

Wolves talk by using facial expressions. *Science Focus*[82] magazine featured pictures of the nine faces of wolves: those being anger, anxiety, curiosity, fear, friendliness, happiness, interest, joy and surprise. Depending on whom you read in the literature, dogs have anywhere from 10 to 100 facial expressions. Maybe, they just learn to copy our expressions. Or, we anthropomorphize them.

Videos show dolphins meal selections by projecting echolocation beams on a screen using hydrophones. They can chose between mackerel and octopus for dinner and even emphasize how strongly they feel about either one. This technology might be used in the future to pick out favorite toys and maybe reveal some innermost emotions. It's called the Elvis System. Dolphins also seem to talk to each other in sentences with clicks and whistles wherein one will remain silent until the other has completed its sentence[83].

---

82 Rosie Mallet "Wolves of Many Faces" Science Focus , November 2018,/ pages 55-59
83 "Mister Buzz Smart Dolphin Answers Questions and Choose Favorite Snack Using Echolocation," Dailymotion, 12/18/2013.

One doesn't need a scientific study to know that pets like birds, cats and dogs talk to each other and sometimes to us. On Spring mornings, the forests are alive with the sounds of birds singing. Later, as the sun sets, the buzzing chants of insect groups step up with a few frogs. Even later, the owls and wolves add their voices.

We know honeybees use dance to communicate, meaning language and possibly thought beforehand. Much of it has to do with food sources. There are two basic forms of dance which change with how far away the food source might be and in what direction. As the dances continue, the excitement spreads and a community dance may follow. Another way bees communicate is by using their antennae to sample pollen that has been collected on a scout's abdomen.

Ten dog barks have been translated by *K9 Magazine*[84]. Being a dog owner, I find their talking the most entertaining. Maybe, I'm wrong, but there are many times I feel certain I know what they are telling me. When my wife comes home, the bark is much higher, almost a squeal; when it's a stranger driving up, suggesting danger (to them), the bark is much lower. When UPS or Fedex pulls away from our house, the dogs sound victorious.

These are the magazine's thoughts:

1. Continuous rapid barking, midrange pitch: "Call the pack! There is a potential problem! Someone is coming into our territory!" Continuous barking, but a bit slower and pitched lower: "The intruder [or danger] is very close. Get ready to defend yourself!"

2. Barking in rapid strings of three or four with pauses in between, midrange pitch: "I suspect that there may be a problem or an intruder near our territory. I think that the leader of the pack should look into it."

3. Prolonged or incessant barking, with moderate to long intervals between each utterance: "Is there anybody there? I'm lonely

---

84 "Why Do Dogs Bark?" April 8, 2016

and need companionship." This is most often the response to confinement or being left alone for long periods of time.

4. One or two sharp short barks, midrange pitch: "Hello there!"
5. Single sharp short bark, lower midrange pitch: "Stop that!"
6. Single sharp short bark, higher midrange: "What's this?" or "Huh?" This is a startled or surprised sound. If it is repeated two or three times, its meaning changes to "Come look at this!" alerting the pack to a novel event. This same type of bark, but not quite as short and sharp, is used to mean "Come here!"

    Many dogs will use this kind of bark at the door to indicate that they want to go out. Lowering the pitch to a relaxed midrange means "Terrific!" or some other similar expletive, such as "Oh, great!"

7. Single yelp or very short high-pitched bark: "Ouch!"
8. Series of yelps: "I'm hurting!" "I'm really scared." This is in response to severe fear and pain.
9. Stutter-bark, midrange pitch: If a dog's bark were spelled "ruff," the stutter-bark would be spelled "ar-ruff." It means "Let's play!"
10. Rising bark is a play bark, used during rough-and-tumble games, that shows excitement and translates as "This is fun!"

And, there's body language to sometimes improve communication, according to Best Friends online[85].

1. Play bow: The rear end of the dog is up, while the front end is down. The play bow generally means: "I want to play."
2. Tail wagging Can mean many things:
    * A low-hung wagging tail could mean: "I am scared or unsure."

---

85 https://resources.bestfriends.org/article/dog-body-language

- A high, stiff wag can mean: "I am agitated, unsure or scared, but not submissive. I might bite you or your dog."
- A loose wag — not really high or really low — normally means: "I am comfortable and friendly."

3. Freeze: Could mean she is scared or guarding something, such as food or a toy, or feels cornered.

4. Rolling over: Can have multiple meanings. Rolling over generally means "I am not a threat." If the tail is gently wagging and the mouth is slightly open, the dog is probably comfortable and asking for a belly rub. If the tail is tucked and the lips are stiff, however, the dog may be scared.

5. Ears perked up: When a dog's ears are forward, he is alert, interested in something.

6. Tail between the legs: If the dog's tail is tucked between her legs and her ears are back against her head, she is afraid and uncomfortable about something.

7. Signs of stress
   - Yawning in new or emotional situations
   - Panting when it's not hot
   - Lifting a front paw as someone walks toward the dog
   - Licking his lips, even though the dog hasn't been eating or drinking
   - Looking away as a person or another animal walks toward him

Squirrels and prairie dogs, which are essentially ground squirrels, have a communication system unique onto themselves, warning the others of the presence of predators. Prairie dogs have dogs standing near the entrances to their holes to "shout" out what kind of predator is coming into the neighborhood.

The chimpanzee named Washoe[86] was taught to use American Sign Language. Although she was able to ask for many items by their

---

86 Clive Wynne,"Do Animals Think?" Psychology Today, November 01, 1999

correct name, trainers were also struck by her ability to combine words/images. That, experts maintain is evidence of thinking. The example often cited is the term "Waterbird" which she coined for a swan. This was a bird type she had never seen before.

Kanzy, a pygmy chimpanzee, could understand sentences. He learned to communicate with symbols during his mother's lessons. One could ask him to pick up a straw and take it to a certain person and he'd do it.

Self Awareness And Evolution

Self awareness is often used to prove thinking and consciousness. It means to be aware that "I" exist and that "I am" separate from those around me. Essentially, to be aware that one is aware. If it came about through evolution, one would assume it came about in small steps. There is no evidence for this. The idea that the larger the brain the better the self-awareness doesn't seem to hold, either. A large brain may help, but it takes something more.

When scientists from the University of South Florida lowered a large mirror in front of some manta rays in an aquarium, they showed an inordinate amount of interest and blew bubbles from their gills. This may be the same as you waving at yourself in a mirror, so-called contingency checking. Experts don't agree. It just as easily could have been interacting with another(perceived) manta ray.

Animals that do show self-awareness include magpies, dolphins, apes, monkeys and elephants. The Red Spot Technique[87] created by Gordon Gallup is sometimes used. A chimpanzee named Megan, who trained with Daniel Povinelli, showed self awareness when an odorless red dot was inked on her forehead under anesthesia. That was done so that she wouldn't know. Researchers kept a mirror in her quarters for months, to prepare her for seeing herself (i.e., if she could). After she awoke and looked in a mirror, she tried to scratch

---

87 Bekoff, M (2002). "Animal reflections". *Nature.* **419** (6904): 255.

the spot off. This was repeated many times with other monkeys with the same result. One might wonder if they could feel it or smell it, but the researchers didn't feel that was the case.

Diana Reiss, from Hunter College of the City University of New York and working at the New York Aquarium[88], discovered that bottle-nosed dolphins also recognized themselves in mirrors. In fact, they recognized themselves at ages that were comparatively younger than humans, i.e., 7 months to 18 months. It's noted that most animals have to grow up faster than humans do.

Signature whistles[89] are often cited as showing self awareness in dolphins. Some researchers are convinced it's them repeating their individual names, maybe: I am, I am, I am. Each dolphin has a whistle that is distinctively their own. Mixed in, however, are whistles common to a particular group. Intensified vocalizations may mean: come, there's more fish here. They don't seem to recognize each other's face, however only their sounds. I once asked a trainer at Orlando's SeaWorld how she knew which dolphin she was talking to and she told me that it was easy, that they all had distinctive faces and smiles. For me, all dolphins look alike.

Since the 1960s, scientists have been seeking ways to communicate with dolphins. Thousands of vocalizations have been recorded, but these sounds are hard to replicate and then there are dialects. Clicks, whistles and slapping their tails are also used, sometimes in concert.

Asian elephants can recognize themselves in mirrors[90], given these mirrors were jumbo-sized, securely mounted and non-breakable. Compact mirror won't do, of course. Instead of greeting the image as they might greet a stranger, they searched the top and

---

88 Morrison R, Reiss D (2018) "Precocious development of self-awareness in dolphins." *PLoS ONE* 13(1): e0189813. doi.org/10.1371/journal.pone.0189813

89 Tyack, Peter L., "Dolphins Whistle a Signature Tune," *Science*, Vol. 289(584), 2000

90 http://news.nationalgeographic.com/news/2006/10/061030-asian-elephants.html

other side with their trunks, as if looking for the other elephant. At some point, however they realized it was themselves. As if posing, they pulled off a few reflections placing their trunk in their mouth or the trunk pulling on an ear. Whenever X's were placed on their foreheads, these were also spotted.

Magpies have been tested with mirrors and red spots, as well. They, too, despite a significantly different brain structure and a much smaller brain than elephants, make an effort to remove the spot when looking into a mirror. That didn't happen when a non reflective metal sheet replaced the mirror.

There is suggestive evidence that many mammals, and dogs in particular, have self awareness by using the sense of smell, not so much visually. We all know a dog shows no interest in his own hydrant work, passing it up and presumably thinking: that's mine. That might be self-awareness. Mine can readily tell if I even grazed another dog, let alone petted one. Chimps will remove chalk marks seen in mirrors. Cats, might know, but act as if they don't care. Typical?

Using a test called Go-No Go[91], Dr. Berns describes a way to teach dogs to retrieve and then teaching them to "no go" if given the signal that they need to give the action some thought. MRIs at the time showed activity in the frontal lobes quite similar to humans. There's a long description in Dr. Berns' book on how to give a dog an order, but have it stay perfectly still inside an MRI. It was impressive work and strongly suggests canine thinking.

Most experts say humans start showing self-awareness most between 18 and 24 months. Researchers use the same dab of color on the forehead. Babies under 18 months may peer into a mirror and visibly enjoy seeing the face, but don't seem to know it's actually their own. That step up to knowing this is your own finger, or toe, or mouth is huge. No one seems to have a good idea how those steps are made.

---

91 Berns, Gregory, *What's It Like to Be a Dog And Other Adventures in Animal Neuroscience*. (Basic Books 2017),20

"Man's faculties for enjoying and producing music must be ranked among the most mysterious with which he is endowed."

CHARLES DARWIN

XIV

The Memory Piece

Memory is another important sign of thinking. It cannot stand alone as proof of thinking and consciousness as virtually all animals display some form of recall. Imagine how it might be if an animal could not remember where it had stashed food or where food and/or water could be found. Or, which wolf was a friend or foe. Or, which penguin is your offspring? No memory of parental lessons and lessons learned would be incompatible with living very long. If, at all.

Most living beings seem to have some form of memory. They have to. Data on how memory may have evolved is relatively sparse. We know that much of our memory lies in the grey matter and that lower species have less grey matter. One might conclude that memory skills, using evolution, improved with time. The problem, in part, is that memory may not totally reside in the grey matter. There are species whose memory seems to reside in different locations, like the tentacles of the octopus and parts of some jelly fish.

Common sense suggests that improved memory, within species, added to natural selection. That is, when they are relevant to survival skills. Mutation probably worked against it.

Microbes Memory

Bacteria appear to have some form of memory. Indeed, all single-celled organisms seem to possess something that is relevant to survival. At times, they know how to avoid adverse situations, find nutrients and stay in safe environments. Been there before? Among some there appears to be collective memories and goals. Certain microbes appear to decide whether they want to use random tumbling or their flagellum (the tail whipping) to move to a more favorable place.

A study by Mathis and Ackerman[92] showed bacteria can learn to survive (possibly meaning remember) better when placed in salty environments if they were first exposed to a milder version of salty in advance. That is, when compared to unexposed bacteria. Certain spore-forming bacteria clearly have a memory mechanism. They initiate the process to form a spore whenever there is a severe, life situation such as extreme cold. To start the process they must recognize the factors and initiate the plan (from memory?). They can survive as a spore in a dormant form for centuries, maybe millennia.

A standout example of bacterial decision-making can be found in the ability of certain bacteria to become resistant to antibiotics. A pathogen (i.e., bacteria that can cause disease) will change from being sensitive to any/every antibiotic to being resistant. Worst case scenario resistant to all antibiotics, which can be a nightmare for patient and doctor alike. Built in as a possible mechanism (?memory) to be drawn on and they actually trade genetic material among themselves to accomplish this. Just how to trade must come from memory.

Most microbes can receive sensory information, integrate it, analyze it, and take appropriate action. Their cell walls or membranes constantly sense their environment (like holding up a moist finger to check the weather), then integrate and analyze information by sending electrical and/or chemical signals internally. A purposeful action follows. Could this mean sentience? Experts say no, but aren't

---

92 Roland Mathis, Martin Ackermann, "Response of Single Bacterial Cells to Stress Gives Rise to Complex History Dependence at the Population Level," *PNAS*, March 7, 2016 DOI: 10.1073/pnas.1511509113

we all chemical/electrical beings? If algorithms only are responsible, evolutionist must explain how so many connecting steps were accomplished.

Do Worms Have Memory Capability?

Worms occupy a peculiar place in the evolutionary tree and some think they are off in a phylum of their own called xenacoelomorpha. They have very unique capabilities. There's a 1959, often-cited experiment by James Vernon McConnell wherein he taught planarian flatworms to contract(out of fear) away from a light. He would shock them just before a light started flashing[93]. He then cut them in half. Both groups regrew the missing half and when complete, both worms would contract (from fear) when shown the same flashing light, without the shock. He also found that when he fed a slurry of the "trained" planarian tissues to whole worms, the cannibal planarians would recoil when shown the same light. So, does this mean, one can eat neurological tissue and retain a memory? Don't try this at home. There are potentially, very serious diseases.

A memory etched in the brain in a worm or other species is called an engram. Researchers in the 1970s have found that dendritic cells "bulk up" when retaining part of a memory in the form of boutons and spines. It's a kind of biological self-wiring and storage units. Locations may vary.

Insects Seem To Have Memory Capability

Depending on which tree of life one follows, insects might be found along our evolutionary path. In this theory insects come from an ancestor called Urbilateria. This creature lived a billion years ago

---

93 Laura Sanders, "Traces of Memory," Science News, Feb 3 2018, 22-26

and may be the ancestor to all species since it had bilateral symmetry. Before then, life forms had irregular and/or amorphous shapes.

Insect brains, when discernible, can be smaller than a grain of sand. What may be construed as a brain, may just be a few ganglia in close proximity. Despite their tiny size, many insects display a terrific memory and suggestions of cognitive skills. Their "mushroom-shaped" brains, when closely examined, resemble our own hippocampus or memory center.

According to an article in *Discover Magazine* by Nicholas Strausfeld, a neurobiologist at the University of Arizona, insects possess "the most sophisticated brains on this planet." Other researcher, Bruno van Swinderen, at the Neurosciences Institute (NSI) in San Diego, says their cognitive functions "are the roots of consciousness." Cockroaches have 1,000.000 brain cells and fruit flies have 250,000 brain cells. When studied under the microscope, neural connections strongly resemble human neural connections. Brains seem to follow similar construction plans.

Cockroaches are the longest surviving species on the planet, going back at least 350 million years with ancestors back another 200 million years. So many fossils of cockroaches were found dating back 220 million years that some scientists call this period the Age of the Cockroaches. Fossils show they had brains 500 million years ago. A study out of Vanderbilt[94] and published in the Proceedings of the National Academy of Sciences showed cockroaches could remember tasks for several days if trained at night. And, they couldn't retain a thing if the training was done in the daytime.

Ants are a great example of intelligence, too. They are able to recall, by using landmarks, where they have foraged without getting lost upon return. They can travel several meters from their home and return with information and/or edibles that can weigh 100x

---

94 https://www.news.com.au/lifestyle/real-life/dreaded-cockroach-is-clever/news-story/ff3a2f21f8cc5cb702d34bb55f3dd6a1

their weight. A collaborative UK project[95] is making drones that mimic this skill so as to avoid problems with GPS.

The honeybee is another good example of an excellent memory. These insects seem to know the time of day and remember locations up to a four mile radius from the hive. They can communicate with other bees as to location of useful flowers. According to Wynne, no other creature besides humans can convey three dimensions of experience to its fellows. Honeybees communicate the distance, direction and quality of food source to their hive mates.

Sniffer bees are being taught, at the University of Konstanz in Germany, to find explosives in land mines by rewarding them with sugar water. They might become the bloodhounds of the future.

Fish Have Memory Capability

Fish supposedly evolved from jawless, armored fish that lived about 530 million years ago. Modern-day lampreys may be their closest representative.

Most researchers think fish have a three-second memory span[96], but they are otherwise dumb. Studies, however show that's a myth. According to Culum Brown from Macquarie University[97], Fish are more intelligent than they appear. In some areas such as memory, their cognitive powers match or exceed those of higher vertebrates including non-human primates.

They have a small brain especially when compared to body size, but they can actually remember some specifics for months. Some fish may be as smart as birds and possibly a few mammals. According

---

95 Wynne, Clive, *Do Animals Think?* (Princeton University Press, 2004), 153

96 "Three-second Memory Myth: Fish Show They Can Remember Things For up to Five Months," DAILY MAIL REPORTER, 7 January 2009.

97 Brown, Culum, Animal Minds: Not Just a Pretty Face." *New Scientist*, 2004, 2451: 42-43.

to a study by Dr. Phillip Gee at Plymouth University[98], goldfish can be trained to touch a lever in their aquarium to receive food. Once established, the feeding time was lowered to a specific hour. It seems as if the fish could tell time. They only touched the handle at the specific time. They would even gather at the handle moments before the time it became functional.

Goldfish memory extends to color recognition. The eye of a goldfish is able to detect red, blue, and green as well as ultraviolet light. Interestingly, researchers at St Andrews University in Scotland found minnows to be at least as intelligent as rats.

A potential boon to fish farms is work done at the Technion Institute in Israel where fish are taught to respond to sounds over a loudspeaker at feeding time. After being released to the sea, they returned, four to five months later; whenever the loudspeaker played the same sounds, they were tricked and harvested. This would save money for aquaculture (fish farming) and help the fish mature as they might normally in the wold.. That is, be healthier.

Reporting on their findings, the researchers said: 'The new method has many advantages. The fish grow in their natural environment, without the use of cages and without environmental pollution."

There are hundreds of articles on fish memory. Rainbow fish can be taught to swim through a single hole in a net and they retain the information for a year. Some fish can use tools. Certain wrasses use rocks held in their mouth to crush sea urchins, clams and scallops. Carp catch on; once caught and released, they become less catchable. Archerfish squirt water to knock insects that has settled on plants extending over the water. One might ask how that came about by evolution. A squirt here and a squirt there, a high-powered squirt, a high-volume squirt? Just trial and error?

---

98 Philip Gee, David Stephenson, and Donald E. Wright "Temporal Discrimination Learning of Operant Feeding in Goldfish (*Carassius auratus*)," J Exp Anal Behav. 1994 Jul; 62(1): 1–13. doi: PMCID: PMC1334363PMID: 16812735

Goldfish can remember tube colors associated with feeding. Paradise fish will avoid places where they've encountered predators. Channel catfish can remember a human voice calling them at feeding time. Many fish can recall competitors (and stay away) who have beaten them in a fight.

The presence of play may mean there's the ability ti think. Elephantnose fish have been observed repeatedly carrying a small ball of aluminum to an outflow tube. And then, when blown away, repeatedly bring it back. White-spotted cichlids have been seen hitting a floating thermometer in an aquarium to make it bob.

Fish supposedly evolved into amphibians such as salamanders and frogs. They came ashore as lungfish able to breathe albeit their lungs were air sacs, only sacs, far different from lungs. The changes to lungs and the ability to exchange oxygen and carbon dioxide had to have had millions of genetic steps, not one or a few changes over night. This needs the "God of the Gaps", too.

Reptiles May Have Memory

Reptiles have lower intelligence than mammals and birds. Their brain compared their body size is quite small with an encephalization quotient(EQ) that is one-tenth that of mammals. Wood turtles can nonetheless navigate mazes better than white rats[99]. Not quite as fast, of course, but maybe more time is needed to think. The largest living lizard, the Komodo dragon is known to participate in play[100], And, play, although not well-documented suggests cognition which indicates intelligence.

Alligators and crocodiles have been seen to balance twigs and small branches (i.e., using tools) on their backs as if these were a branches, to

99 Angier, Natalie (December 16, 2006). "Ask Science". The New York Times. Retrieved September 15, 2013.
100 Tim Halliday (Editor), Kraig Adler (Editor) (2002). "*Firefly Encyclopedia of Reptiles and Amphibians.*" Hove: Firefly Books Ltd. pp. 112, 113, 144, 147, 168, 169. ISBN 978-1-55297-613-5.

lure birds looking for sticks to build a nest. Alligators have been moved as far as thirty miles from their home and yet can travel back across unknown (to them) ponds and swamps to make their way back home. Noted: an 11-foot long gator may have a brain as small as one gram.

Birds Definitely Have Memory Capability

Birds presumably followed reptiles on the evolution scale and that would have been many, many steps up in intelligence. God or too many gaps (steps) to count. The question lingers as to whether dinosaurs were actually reptiles or pre-birds. The general consensus used to be that they were cold-blooded, but if so, one might ask how such a huge animal could quickly warm up each day to regain mobility and other functions. It seems impossible. They must have been warm-blooded, like birds. The discovery that many dinosaurs had feathers with brilliant colors supports this.

Parrots are often listed among the ten smartest animals in the world. If not number one, they are always in the top five. Some owners claim they can carry on actual, legitimate conversations. Ravens, crows, eagles, owls and even ducks can usually be found in the top 25. Virtually all bird types have demonstrated some language and memory skills. Self-awareness remains a challenge to prove, but a German study put a dot on the necks of magpies, who, while looking in a mirror, tried to scratch it off. If the dot were black and not easily seen or felt, no effort to remove it was made.

Studies suggest crows can count up to 3 and parrots up to 6. Cormorants in China, who dive off boats for commercial fish, can count to seven. They quickly learned that they were fed after every seventh fish they brought to the surface. They would actually refuse to dive again unless their neck ring was loosened which allowed them to swallow[101].

---

101 Hoh, Erling Hoh , "Flying fishes of Wucheng – fisherman in China use cormorants to catch fish,". Natural History. October, 1988

There are studies that show birds are able to keep track of the number of eggs in their nest. Many birds can recall where their food caches are stashed. Hummingbirds seem to keep track of the location of the better flowers.

Birds are also known for using tools. The Egyptian vulture uses a rock in its beak to crack an ostrich egg. New Caledonian crows use a beak-held stick to remove insects from logs. Herons use bait to catch fish. Crows in Japan make use of passing cars for smashing dropped nuts. The California scrub jay may show signs of theory of mind, meaning they know what's being thought by others. If observed hiding their cache, they will quickly return to move it.

Mammal Memory

Dogs can be taught the scent of drugs, explosives and/or cadavers, which they easily retain for long periods. They can also smell (discover) TB and cancer in patients. Dogs can retain knowledge of other humans who have cared for them, after a prolonged absence. Just a sniff is needed. A dog can memorize scores of commands and gestures, plus read routine gestures.

Almost everyone has heard the statement that elephants never forget. It may be true, especially under certain circumstances. A 2009 article in Scientific American[102] spoke of two elephants, Shirley and Jenny, who worked together in a circus 23 years before coming across each other again at the Elephant Sanctuary and their excitement to see each other. It was strikingly different than simply putting two elephants (strangers) put together. Three herds of elephants made their way to alternate food and water sources during a severe drought in 1993 in Tanzania's Tanangire National Park. Their matriarchs recalled a drought from 1958 to 1961. Younger matriarchs that

---

102 James Ritchie, "Fact or Fiction?: Elephants Never Forget,"Scientific American, Jan 12, 2009.

were not old enough to recall the previous drought, lost many more calves.

A curious demonstration had urine samples from several other females placed in front of female elephants. They acted up whenever they came across one that did not belong to their herd. Elephants will react poorly to Maasai men who kill elephants, and show no reaction to Kamba men, who do not. They clearly know how to use tools such as switches to scratch itches and blocks to step on to reach high fruit.

Experts say they show empathy, demonstrated by stroking each other when stressed. They clearly mourn their dead. This has been observed many times. They will caress the bones or tusks of their deceased. Sometimes, they even try to bury their dead.

Primates, according to evolution theory, showed up 63-74 million years ago. Determining who were their predecessors remains unclear. Lemur and tarsier-like animals are often cited, but how monkeys evolved into the larger, smarter apes and gorillas is not clear. Why the tail was totally dropped is not known; some argue it basically fell off due to disuse, but this remains unproven. One can cut the tails off of any mammals (like Rottweilers) for generations and the next generation always shows up with tails.

They definitely have improved cognitive skills over non-primate, land animals. They can cooperate to hunt and fight; they can be manipulative and deceptive. Some say they have consciousness. Studies show they have self-awareness.

Chimps, under some circumstances, may have better short-term memory than humans. A Japanese study[103] showed a video to the American Association for the Advancement of Science (2/2012) to demonstrate this. A chimp named Ayumu was able to recall the order of random numbers 1-9 scattered on a screen with blank squares left in their place. A different video shows a PhD struggling to do the

---

103 https://news.yahoo.com/chimps-better-short-term-memory-humans-205822667.html

same. He was successful once in thirty tries whereas the chimp was successful in over 90 percent of his tries from the start. A published critique of the study in Science[104] letters (6/2010) states it has since been shown that humans can match the chimp's efforts if given a chance to practice as he had. Also, the same chimp was able to point out the numbers 1-19 in order, initially scattered across a screen.

Monkeys and apes will beg for food with their hands out, like beggars, along the sidewalks in the Far East. Some will grab food away even while it is partway into one's mouth. Chimps are known for gestures, leading some researchers to suggest man's first language might have been signing. In captivity, chimps can pass on the knowledge of gestures. We know they can recall/recognize faces. Chimps seem to fuss over inequality of rewards when a cage mate is given more in exchange for a token. Orangutans in Borneo use sticks to force catfish from ponds. This must be memory. There's a photograph of a gorilla using a large stick to walk across a body of water,. Presumably, he was checking depth as well as using the stick to check his balance. This, too, has to be a learned skill given to memory.

One might wonder, given evolution, if these limited memory skills could have made the massive leap to human capabilities, by accident. God of the Gaps? **Natural selection cannot add new capabilities unless it is already in the genes. Where would the new blueprints come from?**

---

104 http://science.sciencemag.org/content/328/5983/1228.3

"Robots will be able to do everything
better than us."

ELON MUSK, BILLIONAIRE CEO OF TESLA AND SPACE X

XV
Mechanical Memory

It's clear that a humanoid will need to remember(retrieve) an enormous amount of data to sound like, interact with and function as a normal person. We all retain enormous lists of numbers including phone numbers, ages of our kids, birthdays, and addresses plus all kinds of facts, an enormous repertoire of sights, sounds and smells, events, likes and dislikes, fears, loves, scents, feelings (tactual and emotional)and jokes/puns/quotes.

Memory might be our most prized possession. I've heard older people say that they'd rather go blind or deaf than lose their memories. All of us, I'm sure, would hate to lose the memories of those we've loved and events we've enjoyed. Although these memories tend to fade, they can be retrieved entirely by deeply placed electrodes in a patient's brain. What does that tell us? Are we actually biological video machines, with organic file cabinets, that retain virtually every incident?

Granted, we cannot bring up every speck of memory. That would create enormous clutter and obscure more pressing needs. The brain is conveniently set up to receive, sort and edit a constant cavalcade of incoming information. Probe your mind for a moment about last Christmas; surely a ton of memories will surface. Have your mind go around the dinner table, stop at each face and see what your mind conjures up. You've temporarily or conveniently forgotten a lot.

Most of the hidden data in our brain is seemingly unimportant and useless, but who really knows? Some painful memories are purposefully tucked away in the brain, never to be found again. Childhood traumas are one example. Despite their seeming obscurity, they can have a major impact on life's later decisions, cause phobias, contribute to the selection of partners, contribute to the failure/success of marriages and jobs, result in depression and cause anxiety disorders. How this can re-surface and actually impact us later mostly remains a mystery. How the brain finds the right folder in the right filing cabinet is an unknown. The task resembles an express elevator to the 100th floor of a skyscraper x a million memory files, or maybe ten million. Note this elevator (search engine) must simultaneously go sideways and make loops.

Memory problems for all of us were lessened with his flexible film and camera,. The first cameras were invented by Frenchmen Joseph Nicephore Niepce in 1827 and Louis-Jacques-Mande Daguerre in 1836. The latter individual was responsible for the daguerreotype process of photography that was commonly used during the Civil War days. Select memories could be locked in for many years, but for the aging of film.

Before Eastman's work, the taking and the developing of a picture was enormously cumbersome. It required special glass for negatives, covered with a sticky, colloidal substances involving multiple chemicals. There were many sensitive and complicated steps and it was way too hard for the average person to use.

Cameras steadily improved over years as were different types of film. During the latter half of the nineteenth century moving, serial pictures were invented. Cinematography came about once there was an electric motor. The inventor was William Kennedy Laurie Dickson, an employee of Thomas Edison. His invention, in 1891, called the Kinetograph Camera. The basic mechanism was a window that seemingly opened and closed in unison with a moving, illuminated film. This improved man's ability to further externalize memory.

The first films were black and white, silent and less than a minute long. Many were used for novelty exhibition, only. During the 1890s, however theaters started popping up. Film was sometimes paired up with vaudeville acts. In the early 1900s, artificial light was added as well as screen credits for actors and actresses.

Synchronizing sound with the action was a challenge and it took until 1923 to accomplish "sound on film". The first feature film that was presented as a talkie was *The Jazz Singer* in 1927. It was made with Vitaphone. Two years later, most films had sound. Although color in motion pictures was actually invented in 1908 in England by Albert Smith, the first film shot in color was *Cupid Angling* in 1918.

Films, cameras, projectors, techniques, sound systems and theaters steadily improved until the twenty-first century when there was another big step up to digital movie cameras and digital cinematography.

By 2010, digital movies and cinematography with digital image sensors had pretty much replaced movie cameras and celluloid film. Recording images came in bits and bytes. The resolution in digital film cameras are equal to 35 mm film. Sound has been perfectly in-sync for a long while. Although film stock remains the gold standard, digital camera can function much better in low light conditions. Film stocks and processing remain much more expensive even though film cameras themselves are cheaper. Preservation of films (memories) appears to be best with the older film stocks compared to newer celluloid film. One mostly needs a cold room with the right humidity and the film memories will last 100 years or more. Digital saves the need to upgraded and changed every few years. Cloud back-up can never be guaranteed.

One could, given enormous free time and an endless source of funds record virtually all visual and auditory aspects of one's life. Tactile and olfactory are missing, but maybe not for long.

Mechanical thinking

Depending how one defines thinking, may determine if we believe machines will ultimately be able to think and have consciousness as we do. Humanoids can certainly say: "Yes, I can think", "I gave that some thought" or even "Give me a moment to think that over." Just ask your phone if it can think. My Siri answers: "Why, of course." Any answer given would be a function of algorithms and there are no penalties for lying. Certainly, no remorse. Computers seem to utilize many of the same steps we do when reaching a conclusion. That's, in part, why scientists think we are a more sophisticated versions.

The newest AI machines have incredible memory and language capabilities. Many already have better skills at recalling/retrieving facts (than humans). Their vocabularies are equal to, or better than, any Webster and some dictionary, alone or combined. With the exception of one savant, I know of, no human can translate as many languages as a phone app. No one can calculate as fast as a phone calculator. The savants that come close, often have severe mental deficiencies in other areas. It's as if there's been neurological compromise. Yet, there are a few savants who are entirely functional as well as gifted. How is it that a child prodigy can play the piano or paint like a master at age four? One might conjure up reincarnation. Or, classical piano is in the genes?

To truly think, future machines will have to, according to the experts, have self-awareness and Theory of Mind (ToM). Not be that rooster who looks as his reflection in a mirror and tries to fight with itself.

Can machines ever have self awareness? The answer is a somewhat dubious. No one knows. Certainly, we can give a humanoid video camera eyes that can "see" its reflection in a mirror. It could even say: "I'm that humanoid in the middle of the picture."

Will they have awareness that others around them have awareness, too, sometimes called mind-reading? Again, the answer is hesitant maybe. That said, there's reason to believe machines will ultimately be able to interpret a person's brain waves through electrodes inserted in the brain.

Will machines ever have sentience, meaning feelings? Today, your guess might be as good as anyone else's. Many religious leaders and a fair number of scientists don't think so. All agree, however they will be able to fake it. Humanoids will be able to give a "heartfelt" eulogy, marry couples with tears of happiness and offer reassurance to the seriously ill, any day, any time of the week, as many times as needed. They will have countless numbers of "speeches", in every language, to draw on. **It's all in the algorithms.**

So how did we get into this mess? That is, the potential need to sort people out from machines? It seems inevitable. Might it be part of our genome, a continuance of evolution, a Plan from God, or an enormous mistake?

For now, walking, talking machines are easily discerned and a voice over the phone can be tricked into revealing itself, but these kinds of sorting through all of takers will come increasingly difficult. According to Dr. Rosalind Picard from the MIT Media Laboratory, emotion(s) will have to be programmed. In her book *Affective Computing*, she says: "I have come to the conclusion that if we want computers to be genuinely intelligent, to adapt to us, and interact naturally with us, then they will need the ability to recognize and express emotions, to have emotions, and to have what has come to be called emotional intelligence[105]."

The "father" of the computer might have been the first cave man or cavewoman to say yes or no to a mate. Or, perhaps, it was the hunter who counted saber-toothed tigers in the bushes, on his fingers. That is, if he still had fingers. It could have been an ancient soul who placed large rocks in a row on the ground, to represent tens, and small rocks to represent ones, perhaps to keep track of a

---

105 Picard, Rosalind W., *Affective Computing (The MIT Press, 1998) Preface page x*

trade. Or, the harvest? Or, the number of slaves killed at each event in the Coliseum?

The first computing machine was the abacus which was invented in Mesopotamia circa 500 BC. Originally, this was a flat rock with inscriptions. Today, we know it as a rectangular-shaped apparatus with rows of wires or strings crossing the width, each with sliding, colored beads that represent numbers. It's also called a calculator and it was used across the ancient world until the seventeenth century and is still used in remote areas of China. FYI the oldest surviving abacus dates back to the Babylonian times circa 300 BC Presently, there is a version for the blind. The Sumerian abacus can, by a slight stretch, qualify as a thinking and computing machine since it improved mental skills to handle larger numbers; it could function as a remote memory bank.

Another contender for "the first computer" might be the Antikythera Mechanism. It was found in 1900 inside an ancient shipwreck by Greek sponge divers off the island of Antikythera. It was badly damaged. After restoration of the 30 interlocking bronze gears, it became evident that it had been used to calculate and predict astronomical phenomena, seasons, eclipses of the moon, calendar cycles, and festivals[106].

The slide ruler is an intermediary, computing invention that has helped man to calculate. It was invented by William Oughtred in the seventeenth century, based on work on logarithms by John Naper and logarithm scales by Edmund Gunter. It remained in common use by engineers and select students of science, especially physicists, until the advent of portable electronic calculators. That happened around 1970.

In 1642, French scientist Blaise Pascal invented the first practical mechanical calculator. It was called the Pascaline and he used it to help his tax-collector father. This machine had a series of interlocking

---

106 Simon L. Garfinkel and Rachel H. Grunspan, *The Computer Book* (Sterling Publishing Co. , 2018) 20.

cogs that could add and subtract. In 1671, German mathematician Gottfried Wilhelm Leibniz improved on Pascal's machine with a "stepped drum" (a cylinder with teeth) which persisted for 300 years. This machine could add, subtract, multiply, divide and even do square roots. He is credited with working out the rules for binary math calculations which are still in use today.

Other computer history highlights include French scientist Joseph Marie Jacquard, who, in 1802, invented a loom that used punch cards. In 1822, Englishman Charles Babbage conceived a digital, programmable calculating machine that would eliminate the drudgery out of repetitive calculations. He is considered by some to "really" be the father of the computer. His notes were lost for decades and by the time they were found in the 1930s, much of his thoughts had been invented by others. Ergo, there's a lot of confusion in the texts.

In 1890, Herman Hollerith invented a punch card system to help calculate the 1880 census which ultimately saved the government million dollars and months of tedious work. He called his machine the tabulator and in 1896 he began the Tabulating Machine Company. In 1924, his company became International Business Machines (IBM).

In 1936, Alan Turing, the Englishman who helped break the Nazi code in WWII (see the movie: *Imitation Game*) and thereby changed the course of the war, came up with the idea and plans for what would become the modern computer. It was called the Turing machine and many of his ideas are still relevant today. In fact, there is a Turing test[107] used to determine if one is speaking with artificial intelligence. The test is used in a way to find out whether a computer can be considered intelligent by seeing whether it can sustain a plausible conversation with a real human being. He is considered by many as the "father of <u>modern</u> computing."

---

107 Experts say it can be gamed by deceiving the machine or not answering. An option is the Winograd Schema Challenge which uses ambiguities.

In 1937 an electronic computing machine, the Atanasoff Berry Computer[108], was conceived by Professor John Vincent Atanasoff and his graduate student Clifford Berry. It could do linear equations, but not store data well. It is considered the first machine to use binary arithmetic and electronic switching. In 1990, it was designated an IEEE[109] Milestone. This followed a major patent fight with the makers of the Eniac. Machines such as these used electrical switches to store numbers which essentially set off the digital age. Herein, thousands of switches replaced the rods and wheels of the analog age.

Major steps forward followed the advent of electric communication. In the beginning much of the thinking and planning around computers had to do with military use. Babbage's ideas were designed to lessen the toil and improve the accuracy of artillery firing tables. Toward the end of the nineteenth century messages could be sent in digital form across many miles of wiring. In the 1930s several nations realized these electrical relays could be used for computation. The vacuum tube was invented early in the twentieth century, and by the 1940s these tubes in calculators ran a thousand times faster.

During WWII, Vannevar Bush's US Office of Scientific Research and Development (OSRD) helped steer the development of the ENIAC the first fully electronic digital computer. The inventors Mauchly and Presper made use of Bush's 1927 invention, the analog computer differential analyzer. Notably, the OSRD helped develop radar and set up the Manhattan Project, both of which had enormous impact toward winning that war.

J. Persper Eckert and John Mauchly built the ENIAC (Electronic Numerical Integrator and Calculator) in 1943/44. This is considered the grandfather of all digital computers. It weighed 27 tons and was the size of a modest house at 1800 sq. ft. In 1947 the transistor, replicating the tube, was invented by William Shockley, John Bardeen, and Walter Brittain at Bell Laboratories and in 1958 Jack

---

108 "Milestones:Atanasoff-Berry Computer, 1939". *Global History Network*. IEEE.
109 Institute of Electrical and Electronics Engineers

Kilby and Robert Noyce invented the integrated circuit or computer chip. All this helped enormously, moving the world into the modern era of computers with increasing memory, less costs, more uses, and smaller, more convenient sizes. In 1964, Douglas Engelbart invented the mouse and graphic user interface, sending the world into home computers.[110]

Intel's co-founder Gordon E. Moore stated in 1965 that computer capabilities would improve at faster and faster rates. Moore's law, as it is known now, states: You can place twice as many transistors in an integrated circuit every two years, and they run faster because they are smaller. We now know that theory had limitations. Progress continued at faster rates for a while, but lately it has been slowing.

Shortly after color television arrived, realistic plans for home computers began. Prior to then, very limited, somewhat naive and/or overly powerful variations could only be found in sci-fi entertainment.

One might attribute the first computer in literature to The Engine, an information generator, in Gulliver's Travels (1726)[111]. Gulliver described the machine thusly:

"... Every one knew how laborious the usual method is of attaining to arts and sciences; whereas, by his contrivance, the most ignorant person, at a reasonable charge, and with a little bodily labour, might write books in philosophy, poetry, politics, laws, mathematics, and theology, without the least assistance from genius or study. He then led me to the frame, about the sides, whereof all his pupils stood in ranks. It was twenty feet square, placed in the middle of the room. The superficies were composed of several bits of wood, about the bigness of a die, but some larger than others. They were all linked together by slender wires. These bits of wood were covered, on every square, with paper pasted on them; and on these

110 Xerox® played a major role in inventing the personal computer and laser printer, but failed to market it adequately,

111 Swift, Jonathan, *Gulliver's Travels* (1726). Part 3, Chapter 5.

papers were written all the words of their language, in their several moods, tenses, and declensions; but without any order. The professor then desired me "to observe; for he was going to set his engine at work." The pupils, at his command, took each of them hold of an iron handle, whereof there were forty fixed round the edges of the frame; and giving them a sudden turn, the whole disposition of the words was entirely changed. He then commanded six-and-thirty of the lads, to read the several lines softly, as they appeared upon the frame; and where they found three or four words together that might make part of a sentence, they dictated to the four remaining boys, who were scribes. This work was repeated three or four times, and at every turn, the engine was so contrived, that the words shifted into new places, as the square bits of wood moved upside down."

Very little along this line can be found in the literature until the twentieth century. There's the "Games Machine", a powerful computer in A.E. van Vogt's "The World of Null-A" (serialized in *Astounding Science Fiction* (1945) and, "EPICAC" in Kurt Vonnegut's short story "Welcome to the Monkey House" and novel *Player Piano* (1952). EPICAC was a computer that was designed by Dr. Kleigstadt to solve complex worldly problems and control the US economy. Vonnegut named it after ENIAC. EPICAC ultimately fell in love with its inventor's girl friend Pat. When it realized humans cannot fall in love with machines, it committed suicide by short-circuiting itself. A very sad ending. The number of sci-fi books and films have increased. Many of us probably remember the malevolent and paranoid "HAL 9000" in Arthur C. Clark's *2001*.

How Machines Think

All data is stored and measured in computer bits and bytes (Leibniz's binary system). A bit is simply 1 or 0 (ON or OFF) whereas a byte is a specific combination of bits such as 11000101. (FYI: 8 bits equal 1 byte) Storage can be in megabytes (MB) which is one million bytes or in gigabytes(GB) which is one billion bytes; this goes way up through terabytes (TB) which is another 100OX greater, Petabytes (PB), exa-bytes (EB), Zettabytes*(ZB) and Yottabytes (YB).

Computers work with programs (instructions), sometimes several programs at the same time. These are step-by-step directions much like precise directions you might give a friend to find your home. They process information by accepting raw data (typed or stated input), storing it (memory), "crunching" it (processing, problem solving), and delivering answers (output). Input might come from another computer, one person or several different sources. Processing includes formatting text and correcting spelling/grammar/punctuation when it's a word processor or calculating the moves of a cartoon character for a game - - to name just a few. It's all done to amplify what we do with our minds.

Input into a robot's computer typically comes through outside transmissions, the keyboard, voice commands and/or mouse. Data is used, discarded or stored. The central processing unit or the "brains" of the system is a microchip inside the computer, often cooled by a fan(s). Oddly, our brains require cooling mechanisms, too, just not a box fan. Output can be displayed on an LCD screen, typed by a printer, sent to another computer, transmitted virtually anywhere in the world, encrypted, and/or spoken.

Program terms include software and hardware. The term soft is used because the information is not fixed. It can be changed, improved, trashed or replaced. Hard means permanent. To simplify: the permanent parts (hardware) of your home, within reason, are rooms, doors, walls, windows, floors and roof. Your temporary or changeable (software) parts might be furniture figurines, beds, curtains, hangings, stove and refrigerator. Even your dog or cat.

All humans seem to collect "stuff". In the computer world, we also collect more and more, needing more and more space. We used to use floppy disks (decades ago). That improved with the advent of CDs, and now there are flash drives and cloud storage. A cloud is like having a huge storage unit. By comparison, this is a rental storage unit to the size of a warehouse the size of a continent. Note the route to getting there is the internet.

The "operating system" controls the work: input, storage, processing and output. Memory is a huge part of that, but rather complex for folks who consider themselves to be computer-illiterates. The primary memory system lies in silicon chips, also called integrated circuits. Algorithms are processes or rules to be followed in calculations and other problem-solving tasks.

Input from sensors is sent to microprocessors and running predetermined routines to produce instructions for the robot's actuators to initiate movement/response. There can be simple sensing and processing at the sensory site, but reactions will likely be very simple.

By creating more complex algorithms with learning capability some reactions might become robot-learned from experience[112]. One needn't understand many of the particulars of computers to get the gist. One can ride a horse without knowing how all of the animal's joints, muscles and ligaments work together. The same thinking applies to driving a car or even flipping on a light switch. We all know how to work our way among the Apps on our cellphones, but very few know how that works beneath the screen.

Experts say our brain can store at least one petabyte (1,000,000,000,000,000 bytes) which is 333,333 human genomes or the entire Internet plus some. Other experts think we can actually store much more, in the range of 3-5 petabytes. **The energy needed to store this amount of information in the human brain is often compared to a dim light bulb or 20 watts whereas a computer with the same capacity would need at least one nuclear power plant.**

This is not a static situation. A study by Salk Institute scientists Bartol and Sejnowski in the journal *eLife*[113]: "connections between

---

112 (ElectronicWeekly.com, Glenn Smith, CEO and Co-Founder of MapleBird Sep 9, 2014)

113 Thomas M Bartol Jr et al, Nanoconnectomic Upper Bound on the Variability of Synaptic Plasticity," eLife 2015;4:e10778 DOI: 10.7554/eLife.10778

rat brain cells as a human proxy can change in size (there are 25 strengths or sizes)in a matter of minutes." Also, the dendrites, which can be up to thousands of arms per cell, can vary in length. Plus, there's a variety of types and amounts of chemicals that pass across a synapse. To date there are about 40 different chemicals known. The number of potential mixes of chemicals and their concentrations, electrical charges , ratios and tentacles (arms of the cell) is incalculable.

Artificial Intelligence (AI)

On Feb 11, 2019, President Donald J. Trump signed an Executive Order promoting Artificial Intelligence. He said, "Continued American leadership in Artificial Intelligence is of paramount importance to maintaining the economic and national security of the United States." Elon Musk warns "AI is a rare case where I think we need to be proactive in regulation than be reactive."

When we hear the term Artificial Intelligence or AI, most of us immediately think of a futuristic machine that looks, thinks, talks and acts like a human. In movies, television and novels that kind of image is easy to conjure up. In real life, not so easy To get there the process requires baby-steps and an advanced know-how of robotics, language processing, machine vision, machine hearing, and speech recognition. No question AI is coming. Actually, the basics are already here. It may not look quite human yet, but experts say it will.

Arthur C. Clarke has said that any sufficiently advanced technology is indistinguishable from magic. And so, it seems for most of us whenever we're around a computer, especially one that can drive your car, fly your plane, float your boat, play thousands of favorite songs, warn of intruders, threaten strangers, maybe shoot intruders, write you personalized stories, compose music for the evening or keep a lonely person company. Some say artificial Intelligence will eventually control everything.

Professor Alan Turing once said: "It seems probable that once the machine's thinking method started, it would not take long to outstrip our feeble powers. . . They would be able to converse with each other to sharpen their wits. At some stage therefore, we should have to expect the machines to take over."

Try explaining computers and AI to the average Amazon tribesman. It's hard enough for most of us with an average education to understand the terms let alone how everything works together. We trust our Smart phones to work each day, but very few of us can describe how the innards actually function.

So, what is artificial intelligence. To define the term, one needs to drop back to defining human intelligence and, unfortunately, we don't really have a perfect definition. Someone may seem smart, even have an IQ test that was off the scale, but our measuring tools are primitive at best. We might readily say: "She's really intelligent" based on her level of education, speaking skills and/or accomplishments, but what do we mean? She might lack common sense.

The groundwork for computers began with Claude Shannon's 1937 MIT master's thesis. He suggested electronic circuits could be modeled with Boolean algebra or binary arithmetic (zeroes and ones). His work changed the field of computers drastically and there are some scientists predicting computers will actually become self-aware. In 1943, Warren McCulloch and Walter Pitts, from the University of Chicago, found brain neurons could be modeled by logical expressions, meaning digital. That strongly suggests we use binary methods when we think.

In 1956, John McCarthy, an assistant professor at Dartmouth College, "coined" the term artificial intelligence, separating it from cybernetics. He was a supporter and believer in symbolic logic and believed that computers might be able to simulate all human cognitive capabilities. A workshop followed that summer at Dartmouth. Present were a number of prominent scientists such as Marvin Minsky from Harvard and Nathan Rochester of IBM. Subject matter included neuron nets (machine learning), language simulation, complexity theory, sensory inputs, and randomness of creative thinking. It was funded by the Rockefeller Foundation. The stated goal[114] was: "We propose that a 2 month, 10 man study of artificial intelligence be carried out during the summer of 1956 at Dartmouth College in Hanover, New Hampshire," and "The study is to proceed on the basis of the conjecture that every aspect of learning or any other feature of intelligence can, in principle, be so precisely described that a machine can be made to simulate it. An attempt will be made to find how to make machines use language, from abstractions and concepts, solve kinds of problems now reserved for humans, and improve themselves."

In the 1960s the Department of Defense's DARPA or Defense Advanced Research Projects Agency invested millions of dollars into AI research at MIT, Stanford and Carnegie Mellon University. One of the products that came out of this work was Shakey, who was "the first electronic person", per Life magazine in 1970. Shakey was a rolling cart that could navigate around obstacles.

The public became more aware of the advent of AI computers when they began beating world class experts at games such as chess, checkers, GO and even the tv game Jeopardy. In 2004, DARPA offered one million dollars, in a competition called the Grand Challenge, to the first self-driving vehicle (AI) to finish a rugged 150-mile course. The best that any vehicle did that year, however was 7 miles. The following year, however was different. Stanford University finished first, completing the course in 7 hours, closely followed by two teams from Carnegie Mellon.

One of the goals of AI researchers has been to copy the ways people learn, also called machine learning and neural networks. Data is captured, stored and utilized. Patterns are often used, such as those used with facial recognition programs or for cell cytology in cancer

---

114 J. McCarthy et al., Dartmouth AI Project Proposal; Aug. 31, 1955.

recognition. AI may, in fact, be better than humans when reviewing Pap smears and lung biopsies[115].

Cancerous changes in cells can be subtle and hidden among thousands of cells being surveyed on a Pap smear or tissue biopsy. Computer eyes don't tire after hours or take shortcuts to save time. After the computer sees millions of different views of a man, girl, boy, or woman, whatever, in different poses, from different angles, wearing different outfits, at different ages, different shapes, different sizes, and different hair configurations, it can identify each in future encounters, whether that be in a real photo or actual life.

The "neurons" in computers with AI work as a series of layers, somewhat similar to the layers in the human brain. The lowest level might receive one pixel of a photo, the next several pixels and the top layer puts the whole picture together. If the picture is moving, changing colors, shifting shape and/or changing sizes, the computer must go through separate, connected layers. How it is eventually displayed in our minds is not clear. We know it happens in nanoseconds, arrives in surround-sound and is not like an album that needs pages turned.

To train such a neural network (aka machine learning),one must show the computer millions of pictures of that individual and make it "supervised" or "unsupervised". The former term means it is not told there's a figure in the picture; the latter is told. So, will the training be with humanoids.

Many have concerns that future robots with more sophisticated AI might make decisions to maim and kill humans on their own. **In fact, Elon Musk and Stephen Hawking, plus more than a thousand robot experts, signed a letter in 2015 warning about the development of killer robots.** That, of course, will depend more on who is writing the robot's program than who's signed such a

---

115 Kaiming. He, Xiangyu, Zhang, Shaoqing, Ren and Jean Sun, "Delving Deep into Rectifiers: Surpassing Human-Level Performance on ImageNet Classification, "February 6. 2015, http//arxiv.org/1502.01852

document. Musk has said: "AI scares me to death." There's bound to be malevolent programmers. Just give materials and directions to a modern day terrorist or a rogue regime. All bets are off given another world war.

Both blue and white-collar workers will be affected by AI. The more repetitive the job and/or the less customer or people-involved the more risk. Although a machine with AI can sweep, mop or vacuum, it will have trouble with a smashed, glass vase with flowers spread about the floor. Making calculations of astronomical caliber are easy by comparison.

Millionaire and Chinese AI expert Kai-Fu Lee predicts 40% of jobs will be replaced within fifteen years. Author Dan Brown[116] said on "CBS This Morning" in December 2017 "Man has never created a technology that he didn't weaponize." He also said that AI will become the newest religion, noting how we all look down at smart phones whereas we all used to look up to the heavens, And, indeed, there is even a cyber-religion eyeing the future called Terasem that believes we will eventually be able to live, via AI, forever. People's minds can be uploaded into machines. Their core beliefs include:

I. Life is purposeful
II. Death is optional
III. God is Technological
IV. Love is essential

---

116 Dan Brown is an American author known for his thriller novels, including *Angels & Demons* and *The Da Vinci Code*,

" . . . that DNA is an amazing script, carrying within it all of the instructions for building a human being."

FRANCIS COLLINS, DIRECTOR OF THE HUMAN GENOME PROJECT AND AUTHOR OF *THE LANGUAGE OF GOD*, 2006

XVI
Our Piece

Our brain is a three-pound, biological machine. Memory is a combination of processes where incoming information is sorted, trashed or retained, time-marked, encoded, linked, stored and used immediately or retrieved as needed. Our memory capabilities are at their best, and perhaps their fastest, when we are infants, absorbing like a dry sponge. With increasing age, the capacity to store and retain information seems to slow down. Seniors, thinking the reason storage space is used up, hope that it is replaced by wisdom. Retrieval processes are sometimes slowed and the ability to memorize are a bit hampered.

Without memory capability the human species could not have survived. Imagine stepping in the same hole every day and twisting the same ankle, over and over again. Or, not recalling the caveman who clubbed you over the head last week just dropped in for a chat.

No question, memory is vital to our existence. Is it there by accident? Notably, both hardware and software actually kick in long before we are born. Studies show newborns recognize their mother's voice, immediately. Newborn infants arrive with sucking instinct (memory or instinct of both). Their bodies also have memory (instructions) how to swallow and digest the milk. And, poop. Social media has a video of a baby crying whenever any stranger holds her, but abruptly stops and seems to smile when the man, who is the recipient of her mother's heart transplant, holds her and she presumably hears her mother's heart. The mother had died during delivery.

Memory helps us retain and utilize language, interact with others and perform different tasks. One cannot simply say a few words, read a sentence, and/or make a phone call without the use of memory. Not only does one need a stored memory on how the phone works (which "buttons" do what), but also know whether it is ON or OFF, how to connect with the outside world, what different outcomes mean, such as a busy signal or request to leave voicemail, who will be on the other line and why you're calling. Imagine living with any one of these deficits. As of now, we all have to recall at least ten personal phone digits and scores of other phones, three to six personal address digits and several other addresses, time digits, temperature digits and meaning, PassWords and UserWords, several email addresses and scores of birthdays. That ability did not roll out piece by piece.

Just the function of talking requires "muscle" memory on how to use the neck muscles, tongue muscles, vocal cords and breathing, how to select words in a particular order (past, future and present tense), use the appropriate volume and tone, add in inflections, and understand the conversation. And, that's just a minute chunk of a day. Memory requires many different modules of memory working together, changing and moving in and out. As you read this book your thoughts and feelings run together, seemingly very smoothly, but they are actually separate electrical swirls that intermittently meld together easily.

In his famous dialogue: Theaetetus, concerning the nature of knowledge, Plato (427-347 BC) likened memory to an aviary and thoughts as being different kinds of birds flying about. How one grabs the right bird (memory) is not clearly revealed. Of course, he knew nothing of engrams, nucleotide bases and neurons. In his time, emotions came from the heart.

The ancient Greek philosopher Aristotle (384-322 BC) was keenly interested in man's memory. He likened our mind to a blank slate at birth. Memories were said to be similar to impressions in a wax tablet. This theory was utilized for centuries and was called "the storehouse metaphor".

Wilhelm Wundt and William James, both considered founders of modern psychology, studied memory, and James actually discussed the possibility of neural plasticity[117]. German philosopher Herman Ebbinghaus described learning curves and forgetting curves in the mid-1880s. German biologist Richard Semon in 1904 proposed memories of experience can be found in engrams within the neurons of the brain. In the 1940s the field of neuropsychology emerged as well as a biological basis for encoding. That was after there was considerable debate, as to where memories actually reside, i.e. in nerves, in branches, and/or involving different nerves. It was known that when specific areas of the brain are injured or stroked, the person will lose select memories and/or skills related to past experience. Youngsters can sometimes recoup those skills due to plasticity.

In 1949, Canadian Donald Olding Hebb said that neurons that fire together are wired together, meaning memory has much to do with neurons that are connected (called **Hebb's rule**). This has been supported by many subsequent studies. In 1968 the Atkinson-Shiffrin[118] model or multi-store model of memory was proposed. It basically says there's a sensory register where information first enters and it basically is released or stored as short term and long term. The 1970's brought the misinformation effect from the Elizabeth effect[119] and the encoding specificity principle of Endel Tulving. Today, studies on human memory fall into the cognitive sciences.

---

117 Plasticity is the capability to learn (add connections such as dendrite spines) and to relearn after such things as head injuries and strokes.

118 Atkinson, R.C.; Shiffrin, R. M. (1968). "Chapter: Human Memory: A Proposed System and its Control Processes". In Spence, K. W. ; Spence, J.T. The Psychology of Learning.,. New York: Academic Press. pp. 89–195.

119 The tendency for post-event information to interfere with the memory of the original event.

The current ("classic") teaching is that humans have three types of memory: short-term, long-term and working, but maybe there should also be a subset under short term called fleeting.

Fleeting memory is the type of memory that only lasts a few seconds, typically does not impact one's life, and is not embedded for future retrieval. One might compare it to disappearing ink; that is, write a thought down with this unique ink and watch the words disappear. A comparable life situation might be passing a specific stoplight, among many stoplights that you might pass on your drive to work or school. Normally, you would not specifically recall whether that light was green or red a few miles later. Nor would you recall the type of car in front and/or beside you.

If a cop were to stop you for running that light, however, you should still remember. You might also recall that several cars followed you through the same light and that it was actually yellow. If there's no cop, that information dissipates. The brain considers this information unimportant and discards it rather quickly, along with billions of other bits, all day long. What your left knee is doing this moment is useless information to be discarded unless something draws your attention down there.

Different parts of your brain are always watching, analyzing, listening, measuring, comparing, smelling, tasting and feeling all parts of the world around you, nanosecond to nanosecond, 24/7. This is done in an erasable or disposable, playback mode, constantly adding new and subtracting old information. There's no need to remember whether the slice of Swiss cheese on your sandwich was thin or thick yesterday. If something important happens, the brain marks the biological disc or tape in some fashion and sets up a new storage site (a new dendritic bump, perhaps) among the billions of dendrites (branches) found on nerve cells. Electronic images do not occupy much space.

Imagine having every room in One World Trade Center stuffed with overflowing file cabinets and you need a very specific file that can be found somewhere on those 104 floors and you need it in the next second or two. This would be a physical impossibility without the use of a computer(s). Even then, knowing and retrieving may take a while. Your mind can also retrieve a comparable file easily in much less than a second. How it is indexed and retrieved so quickly remains a mystery. There are no 10K runners.

The difference between short term and long term memory breaks down into where, how long and what way a memory will be stored. The short term type tends to dissipate, decay, degrade, and/or erase in hours to days. It blurs easily. You might remember a burgundy BMW that clipped your car for a long while, but if it just cut you off, the memory might last an hour or a day at the most.

Long term memory may stay with you for decades. Even, for life. Try singing a popular song from many years ago without a prompt. Most likely you cannot, but if it's playing on an AM station, you can easily sing along. The words simply show up. Watch a great movie from eons ago and see what you suddenly remember as the scenes progress. You'd be surprised what's stored deep inside.

There are some special, savant individuals with autism who can remember incredible details[120] such as precisely drawing a many-block New York City scene with skyscrapers, after one helicopter flight over the area. The most famous savant might be Kim Peek, who was copied for the movie *Rain Man*. He was considered a MegaSavant by some. He could read both sides of a thick book at the same time, left eye on left page, right on right, in less than an hour, and retain more than 98% of what he read. He retained tons of baseball scores as well as entertainment and political facts. He actually lectured (traveling with his caretaker father) around the world, appearing at lots of universities. He (or his father) would challenge anyone in the audience to ask him any question re data. He could recite paragraphs, even

---

120 Dr. Darold Treffert , *Extraordinary People: Understanding "Idiot Savants"* (Harper and Row, Publishers 1998).

correcting the author if the date was wrong, from any book he had ever read. He could even recite, if asked, to recall what's on page number XYZ. And, that was after reading thousands of books. On tour, college students would often challenge him with facts from any book he had read and his recall was always right.

Although he delighted it spouting the facts, living life was a huge challenge. Kim was born without a corpus callosum in his brain. That's the connection between the right and left brain, essentially making him a natural, split-brain individual. He resembled a spectrum individual, but not quite autistic. He spoke and acted much like a child. He couldn't tie his own shoes without help from his dad who took him on these tours.

On the other side of the coin there are a few high IQ, normally functioning savants like Akiane Kramarik. Now in her early twenties, she has been drawing since age 4 and painting since age 6. Her most famous painting, done at age 8, is Prince of Peace. This piece is amazing. Her first completed self-portrait sold for $10,000 USD. She is an author of a best selling book, a poet and a musician/composer. She has appeared on many national TV shows including Oprah. She is a polymath to the extreme, yet her brain is no larger than yours or mine.

Unless you or I (normies, I hope) make a point of studying all night for a final exam, memorizing the lines of a play, sing a song repeatedly, see a movie several times, become a victim of a crime, or closely follow a news story on television, we cannot come close to a savant's skills. Try telling someone the five main news stories from a week ago. There are reports of individuals becoming savant-like after head injuries. One man was hit on the head with a baseball bat and ever since could tell you which day of the week a specific date falls on, going back decades.

I'm not sure the fun or adoration is worth the exchange of mental functions, lost by taking a bat to one's head, and hoping to hit the right spot(s). So, as they say, do not try this at home on your own. A few people, who have had strokes, suddenly discover that they could paint like a master when they had never painted a canvas before. Something is going on in our brains also yet to be explained. Note, the vast majority of strokes and head injuries result in minimal problems to major deficits, never improvements. No one, I know of, has knocked sense into somebody.

There's an unclear line where, how and when a short-term memory becomes long-term and what the mechanism might be. We know nerve cells change, but how and why remains a mystery. There has to be a mechanism, however. Perhaps, it's like a football helmet that gets a star decal every time the player scores a touchdown. Facts beget new additions to new cells.

Working memory helps us learn, use math, read, use tools, draw on past experiences, and apply knowledge. Repetition of actions or thoughts lends itself to making new neural pathways (new wires) in the brain. Like adding another file cabinet to your office. Once you learn to ride a bike, you never forget. The same applies for use of silverware, chopsticks, cups and glasses.

An astronomical number of memories exist in our brains. Memories on how to do things, and how not to do other things, what to say and when not to say. Some are stills and some are video. If one buys a self-assembly office desk (DIY), the mind brings forth the means to read and understand the directions, follow the plan(s) and how to use tools. How to turn a screwdriver is a memory. And, when to stop turning. One doesn't need to learn to type every time they sit in front of a keyboard. Visual memories can incorporate familiar scenes. Hearing noises may bring visual memories.

Different brain functions include memory, arousal/sleep, attention, consciousness/thought, decision making, executive functions, language, motor function, sense function and perception (senses). Some of these have specific locations in the brain (central offices), and some involve more than one location (satellites?). Virtually any and all functions can work together to initiate, help, or modify actions or favor inactions. Nearly all overlap in many ways. What may seem incredibly fast is actually incredibly slow in the grand scheme of things such as the speed of sound, electricity and light.

Thinking is what helps us make sense of the world around us safe. Little needs to be said what life would be about without that capability. Only ours can be done in the abstract.

Memory itself can be broken down into smaller components. Declarative and spatial memory generally arises in the hippocampus, deep within the brain. Emotional memory often lies within the amygdala. The latter was evident in the case of Henry Molaison, an epilepsy patient in the 1950s who had this area of his brain "scooped" out. He lost the ability to store new information. Yet, these kinds of patients, who cannot retain recent memory, can often times remember self-care items like brushing one's teeth, how to bathe, conversational skills and even how to ride a bicycle or horse. These memories must be housed elsewhere.

The Henry Molaison case from 1957 changed how scientists viewed memory. This patient suffered from severe epilepsy after a bicycle accident at the age of nine. Because he was incapacitated by uncontrollable seizures, neurosurgeon William Beecher Scoville tried a new approach; he removed the temporal lobes and parts of the hippocampus and amygdala on both sides of his brain. His epilepsy did improve, but Molaison lost the ability to form new memories. He did remember his name, family members and childhood events, but nothing brand new. If given a list of words, he would forget them in about a minute's time. He would even forget that he was even given a list. This gave researchers evidence that short-term and long-term memory are, in fact, two different processes and in different locations.

In 1987, a severe nerve poisoning occurred on Prince Edward Island. It killed three and sicken dozens, many of whom had seizures. Some of the latter folks permanently lost the ability to retain recent memories. As one might expect, this caused enormous problems for the patients and the families through the years. This handicap is called Amnesic Shellfish Poisoning(ASP). It affects the hippocampus in the brain. The toxin is domoic acid which has caused similar memory problems in people who have eaten mussels, clams and oysters along both US coasts at worrisome times. It has even happened to some who have eaten the parts of crabs who have fed on these shelled-species.

Domoic acid is not heat sensitive, meaning cooking will not destroy it. One can only be cautious as it is undetectable. Certain months of the year are more risky than others. Don't count on the cook knowing. If the food came straight from the docks and into the freezer, there's no date, no way to even know. Ever since I learned about this, I have avoided most shelled animals.

ASP happened to sea lions in Monterrey, California, in 1998, after eating sardines and anchovies. Many were found wandering on streets, falling over and confused, collapsing in a quivering mass. Their bodies were full of pseudo-nitzschia, a phytoplankton which manufactures this poison. Sea birds have been known to be poisoned and stories exist that these changes inspired Alfred Hitchcock for his movie *The Birds*.

I once had a patient with a stroke in one area responsible for retaining short term memories. He could not remember, day-to-day, why he was admitted to the hospital or who I was. Every morning he acted as if I were a new doctor assigned to his case. I had to introduce myself over and over again as well as explain what was going on with his care. This was done in depth, from day one. At times, it was exasperating. Every morning he would get angrier and angrier, demanding to know why he was being kept in the hospital, and saying no one was telling him a thing(including me). He was told repeatedly by all, but to no avail. His diagnosis, test results and progress were even written on a whiteboard across from his bed and, later, on a sheet of paper taped to the meal table in front of him. None of this changed things. One morning, he demanded that his family get him a new doctor. The next day he forgot the previous demand.

I found it interesting that he knew how to use a knife and fork. He could read books and understand tv shows. He couldn't tell you a thing he learned in the news, however, moments after the story passed. He remained that way until his dying moments.

Sensory memories can be broken down to what has been seen (visual), heard (auditory), smelled (olfactory), tasted (gustatory), and/or felt (tactile) plus others. You may not remember how good (or bad) your morning coffee tasted last month (each cup being a fleeting memory), but you will likely recall the scent and taste of coffee forever. Likewise, you may not remember the taste of the orange you ate last week, but you will always remember the taste. Under some circumstances, the scent of Thanksgiving pie the taste of turkey, these may bring forth an image of holiday dinners and conversations with friends and family from many years ago.

Topographic or spatial memories are constantly changing. They tell you where you are located in a room, such as midway between two walls, seated in a chair, in front of a desk, with the door open or closed. But, not always. You changed chairs or you stood to speak. This memory keeps track of where you are seated, how high, how close to the table, like a personal GPS system.

Flashbulb memory is an indelible mark of sorts left in the brain that occurs when something wonderful (like a surprise party) or extremely bad(death of a loved one) happens. Older folks can relate exactly what they were doing and where when they learned of President Kennedy's assassination. Fifty-five years later, I can still see the hot dog stand and the line I was standing in when someone in the stand mentioned the assassination. They had a radio on. I skipped the hot dog and hurried to a nearby sorority house to watch the news.

The same flashbulb memory happened to many of us when Neil Armstrong took man's first steps on the moon. Almost every adult knows what they were doing when the Oklahoma bombing happened and/or especially when the World Trade Centers were struck. Most of us, those who are married, can vividly recall, and replay, our wedding night or other times when a loved one died or a child was born. These are sometimes also called episodic memories.

Autobiographic memories overlap, but may involve the more mundane such as buying one's first home, first bike, one's first car, graduation from high school, a first love and so on. There are semantic memories that have to do with the use of language, mathematical memories used to balance checkbooks and addresses, and procedural memories that recall how to ride a bike or swim in pool.

How Do Humans Think?

To think, as we humans do, one needs most, if not all, of that three-pound biological machine carefully locked in and protected inside our skulls. To correctly think, or think correctly, has varied definitions. Regardless, our brain needs to be self-aware, be aware that others around you think (the theory of mind), and to use some form of language as a tool.

The "Einsteins" of the world, contrary to popular thought, do not have larger brains; and, to the contrary, most of the mentally handicapped do not have smaller brains. The brain is likely kick-started at the moment of conception, just as the heart, liver, kidneys and all organs have their beginnings. The brain is completed in about twenty years. It will have 37,500,000,000,000 cells (large parts), give or take ten million, and uncountable cellular, connecting, smaller parts. Size may not matter when it comes to IQ. This may have more to do with how closely the cells are packed or how the connections are made. To know this, just compare the smarts of a chihuahua brain with a great dane brain.

Like taking a clock apart to see how the brain works, we could approach this problem by dissecting it by sections: like the occipital lobe for seeing, temporal lobe for hearing and frontal lobe for thinking. But, there's little explanation how thinking works, Even if we dissect these subsections down to the cellular level, an explanation cannot be found. Each of these "parts" have even tinier parts within such as the nucleus, chromosomes, nucleolus, mitochondria, Golgi apparatuses, mitochondria, endoplasmic reticulum, lysosomes, tubules as highways and a semi-permeable, cell wall. Notably, these inner parts have billions of tinier makings including the cytoplasm, DNA or six billion nucleotide bases, thousands of RNA molecules, tens of thousands of proteins, and uncountable numbers of enzymes. We will quickly learn, that the more parts we tease out, the harder it becomes to understand how they could possibly work altogether. Maybe there's an invisible force.

Perhaps, working from the "ground up" makes more sense, i.e., like building a clock from a kit. At conception 23 strands, half of his 23 helical chromosomes, and half of her 23 helical chromosomes come together to form a blue print (23 complete helical chromosomes) which contain all the instructions for what, how and when to do things and what, how and when to not do everything human. Within, are all the instructions to build and maintain a brain. Somehow the responsible cells group together and follow a plan. They all know where to go and what to do when they get there.

To envision this beginning when the half-chromosomes link together, think of an enormous zipper that stretches from Manhattan to Manchester. This zipper is much faster the jet train. It can zip shut in a "supersonic" fifteen minutes or less. Each chromosome was virtually helpless, but once the different parts are zipped together, they will rule that individual's universe. They will be able to forecast, plan, predict, set up and control everything specific to that human, e.g. whether that be this person's sex, whether he/she will be tall or short (and how tall or short), which race or a mix, have a high IQ or be average, be blond or black-haired (etc), be right-handed, left-handed, or ambidextrous, prone to select diseases or not, and whether they will become a compassionate person or an arrogant putz. Everything will rollout in an incredibly, orderly fashion. Forensic scientists are already finding this pre-set, personal information by using DNA found at the scene of a crime.

Although the minute portions of DNA from the crime scene are studied, a geneticist can make a good guess of the perpetrators's facial appearance, hair color, eye color and race. The Golden State killer is a prime example. His eventual phenotypic drawing was picture perfect of him as a younger cop. Further analysis and comparisons connected authorities to relatives and then the killer.

An interesting question is whether all plans, regardless of timing, are present from the very start and roll out at later dates as needed. Indeed, how much of "evolution" is already recorded in the blueprints. For example, perhaps ID wrote the plans for pre-humans to eventually lose body hair, walk more erect and think more deeply.

By twenty-four hours after conception, the egg starts forming the neural tube (nerve tissue) or ectoderm. The earliest cells seen are stem cells; they will eventually form the entire neurological system, the nerves from the brain to the tip of the toes, to ears, eyes and nose, to all aspects of the digestive system, to the heart and all blood vessels, to all lymph nodes, to all organs, to every bone and to all connective tissues. The brain becomes the master puppeteer.

The brain begins as a submicroscopic speck, yet somehow it knows how to become a resilient, self-repairing, self-wiring, constantly learning and self-correcting organ. It may be the seat of one's spirit or soul, but no one knows how that works. The brain is always strategically located just behind the eyes, perhaps to see quickly. It contains all of the master controls, starter logs and circuit breakers. Like tentacles, long nerve cells reach out from different parts of the brain to the extremities, organs, endocrine organs, the immune system and all sense organs. Reciprocal systems are set up and maintained.

Every nerve cell has been given a specific job to do, a place to set up and a job assignment. Virtually all cells are two way, info-streets, at a minimum.

At one point, billions of neurons in the brain migrate, sometimes as many as 250,000 per minute; they go to predetermined locations, some of which are far away by cellular standards. They are guided by programming and chemical signals, sometimes climbing the long arms of glial cells and bailing at pre-determined heights. Despite the distances, they set up housekeeping at very specific locations. No one knows how this is so well controlled and coordinated; it is obviously purposeful and organized. No detail is left to chance.

One might compare these migrations to the Boston marathon with a billion runners, each given a different route and destination. A few runners simply need to run down the street or around a block or two while others have to scramble for tens of miles. Some climb ropes of different lengths hanging from skyscrapers, others follow Interstate highways, swim across rivers, or drop down manholes.

Certain kinds of structural cells may send out guiding signals. When the runners (neurons) reach their designations, they each reach out with dozens(+) of arms/hands (tentacles) that connect with dozens of dozens of other arms/hands (tentacles) already in place. Each connection can communicate by the use of one or more of 40+ potential chemicals (e.g., dopamine) in different combinations and concentrations. Altogether, the messaging capacity of these trillions of cells is near-infinite. The rules for transmission and reception are ingrained.

The function of both sides of the brain is well stated by Dr. Reeves and Swenson in a 1995 text: ". . .the capacity to express appropriate feelings, appetites and drives; the capacity [for] ... learning, memory, logic, etc.; the capacity to maintain appropriate thresholds and tolerance for frustration and failure, and to recover promptly from their effects; the capacity to maintain effective and well-modulated defense reactions (i.e., repression, denying, pretending, rationalization, blaming, withdrawal, fantasy, depersonalization, obsessive-compulsive behavior and bodily reaction patterns involving alimentation, respiration, metabolism, etc.).”

Dr. Harold Wolff[121], a famous neurologist, was quoted as saying: “We all know we think, or think we think”, but we don't really know how we think. If we were a machine, this function might be traced to specific mechanical, electrical switch and/or chemical factor, but not so in people. At least not yet?

Where in the brain we “think we think” resides is unknown.

Oddly, the right side of the brain controls (motor and sense) the left side of the body and the left side controls the right side. Why the two spinal tracts (pipelines of billions of nerves) literally crossover remains a mystery. **This might be the one of the most important findings that refutes the theory of evolution. There is no apparent evolutionary benefit. It could not have happened (and did not) by small steps. I cannot find a reasonable evolutionary explanation in the literature.**

If one injures or strokes the right side of their brain, the paralysis shows up in the left leg or arm or both. This opposite anatomy suggests the spinal cord twisted 180° at very early point following conception. It sets up seemingly illogical pathways. One would think the right side of the brain would rule the right side of the body, left for the left, but that isn't the case. To my way of thinking, there must be a very good reason, just we haven't found it yet. In some ways the combination of two hemispheres act like two individuals who came together to make this machine(human) work. The two sides complement each other in many activities and emotions. Could the Lord's prayer, which begins “Our Father. . .” mean the father of our two parts?

In addition, **half of each eye is innervated by a different half of the brain. When you look left, half of the eye is right brain and**

---

121 Dr. Alexander Reeves and Dr. Rand Swenson, *Disorders of the Nervous System: A Primer* (Imperial Company Printers, 1995)

half is left brain. Evolution cannot explain this. How does the spine twist 180 degrees and only half of these nerves twist? In addition, none of the other cranial nerves changed sides.

We can tell, by using the functional Magnetic Resonant Imaging (fMRI), if a patient, who seems to be in a vegetative state (dead-like), actually has feelings and relevant thoughts. That means the person is not really dead. He/she is trapped in a neurological cage. Might this be similar to an animal who has inner thoughts, but cannot express them as we do? We don't know.

In 2008, Jack Gallant at the University of California, Berkeley improved brain decoding by measuring activity in the visual areas of the brain. His team could tell what the person was looking at, and after further research, he could translate the discrete image. This says it's not such a wild thought to say that scientists will be able to read a person's thoughts in the future. The question remains how detailed, how personal and how soon. And, most importantly, by whom.

One wonders if cavemen thought about whatever they needed or what they were about to do before they had language skills? One would think the first true humans were able to think at least as well as or better than animals did at the time. Whether one believes in evolution or Intelligent Design, there must have been some level of thinking. Evolution would say it happened very slowly, but the theory lacks the explanation of how. Common sense suggests tool-making and cave drawings alone required thoughtful preparation.

Another question might be how do deaf people think, and talk to themselves (do they have that "inner voice", too), especially those who have been deaf since birth and have never heard a spoken word. There's no question they think. Helen Keller, despite being unable to hear or see, was an incredible intellect. Many texts discuss this issue and it turns out the deaf have an inner voice compatible with sign language. How the deaf-mute thinks remains unclear.

Author Temple Grandin who is a professor of animal science at Colorado State University, an author, a TV personality and an autistic person, says she thinks by using images, not with language. She has a "video library" in her head and uses the example of a dog; she can rapidly conjure up images of every dog she has ever met. She says she can tell what animals are feeling and thinking, especially fear, and, in having that skill, she has made the wholesale slaughter of cattle more humane[122]. Those who have been exposed to voice either by implants, surgery, or late arriving deafness have an inner voice. Once you have one (or two, or three) you retain it(them).

Albert Einstein was once quoted as saying: "I very rarely think in words at all. A thought comes [to me], and I may try to express it in words, afterwards."

Language gives most of us symbols(letters, numbers, pictures, etc.) for ideas and these allow for abstraction and reflection. Noted, words, of a sort, travel inward from our eyes, ears, and nose to our brain. These messages come as light waves, sound waves, skin pricks and scented particles. The brain converts them into real words, thoughts and actions.

The biology of thinking might be defined as a series of ideas in a specified arrangement. The arrangements can be modified by emotions and personal agendas. Yet, there is no consensus for a clearcut definition. That's because it is multifactorial and not measurable like inches, meters, liters and temperature. The brain can cut and paste, delete, add on and add punctuation.

When it comes to pain, as a physician, I can only ask my patient how bad is it, from one to ten, with ten being the worst. Or, ask someone to grade the intensity of their feelings: how intense the hate, love, and fear, for example. That's harder to do and harder to understand. Is your hate merely a 2 to 3 today? Describe what love actually feels like without making any comparisons or citing physiological changes.

---

122 Verlyn Klinkenbor. "What Do Animals Think?" Discover website(May 01, 2005).

According to Charles Q. Choi in 2013, a writer for *Scientific American*, using brain scans, scientists are on the verge of seeing some of our mental images. They gave volunteers fictional characters to envision and then studied their brains. Results showed that different parts of the front and middle brain lit up. Theory suggests we keep these images in these particular areas and that memory is revised, edited or extended with time as needed.

According to Laura Sanders, a correspondent for *Science News*, our brain acts like a film editor. She cited a study done by Ben-Yakov[123]. The hippocampus, which is a small segment deep inside the brain, may literally slice up our continuous existence into scenes (logical sizes) suitable for storing memories. This is supported by functional MRI studies.

We comprehend by processing information, giving it thought and recognizing our role, whether to become active or passive. To help make this decision, we use brain specific functions such as memory, pattern(s) recognition, problem(s) solving, mental imagery, language, judgment, critical thinking and relevant associations.

Babies don't understand the world about them when they first arrive, yet by throwing out an invisible net(s), they capture and analyze everything that comes their way, and then some. Virtually all of this is done in the subconscious. Some of this happens before birth while in utero. We know this because babies will recognize their mothers voice shortly after they arrive. Babies might be able to handle all incoming, but as we age the brain must become more selective.

Early childhood also plays a critical role. Jean Piaget(1896-1980)[124], a Swiss psychologist from the twentieth century, is known for the

---

123 A. Ben-Yakov and R. Henson, "The Hippocampal Film-editor: Sensitivity and Specificity to Event Boundaries in Continuous Experience". The *Journal of Neuroscience*. Published online, October 8, 2018. doi:10.1523/JNEUROSCI.0524-18.2018.
124 https://en.wikipedia.org/wiki/Jean_Piaget

Theory of Cognitive Development, which, to this day, explains these important stages. Noted, he has said that animals go through the same early stages, much more rapidly, as survival is truly at stake. We continue to "develop" whereas they slow down and usually stop.

Piaget's four stages are sensorimotor, pre-operational, concrete operational and formal operational. Sensorimotor stage goes from birth to age two (or the acquisition of language). Children are very egocentric. They learn about the world through their movements and senses. Pre-operational covers age two or the beginning of talk to age seven. Herein is the heavy use of symbols to represent the world, like drawing, the slow increase in reasoning, wanting to know why things are the way they are. Concrete operational stage goes from age seven to eleven and herein children begin to think logically and slowly become less egocentric. Formal operational stage, age eleven to sixteen, shows increasing ability to think abstractly. They acquire metacognition which is the professional term for thinking about thinking.

Human babies start showing self-awareness between the ages of 15-24 months. The noted "rouge test" involves putting rouge on the nose of a baby and seeing if he/she will wipe it off when looking in a mirror. Prior, they might point at the mirror, but not try to wipe off the red spot. This, roughly, is the highest level the smartest animals, at least on land, seem to reach.

Within this age range, they respond to their name and if speaking, can refer to themselves using their own name. They may use the word "I" or "me" appropriately. They may express personal likes and dislikes. And, everyone knows that they learn the word "No" around this time, meaning I don't want that. There almost always an emphasis on I.

Is God of the Gaps playing a role?

A human baby actually communicates long before it speaks. A cry might mean a wet or dirty bottom, tired, hungry, coldness and/or a need to be held/loved. The caliber and intensity of the sounds can have different meanings. Moms and dads can often tell what their child is "saying", but strangers might be at a loss, especially those who have never had children. None of it appears to be a random sound, which is proven by the fact that if the need is met, the crying ceases. Noted they recognize parents and sometimes other family members, but respond differently when addressed by strangers. Perhaps, they somehow know a stranger is not as safe. Inborn design? No one teaches them this. This seems like purposeful, genetic design.

Body language also speaks. All moms know the look of fear, anger, frustration and happiness on their baby's face and/or the way they shake their arms. Some say, a smile is worth a thousand words. Babies seem to focus on mom's voice and sometimes dad's voice as if they are working hard to learn their language. Trying to make sense out of what seems nonsensical at first. Once they can speak, the questions come out at blazing speed.

Babies have the remarkable built-in skills to understand and ultimately speak any language, no matter how complex it might be, from Chinese to Hebrew, English to Russian. In fact, a child can even grow up understanding and speaking more than one language. Folks with the ability to speak, read and understand multiple languages are called polyglots or multi-linguists. The record holder for spoken languages is Emil Krebs (1867-1930), a German diplomat, who spoke 65 languages. Supposedly, he bragged about all of his prodigious profanity skills.

Our brain has an uncountable number of built-in timer mechanisms. We sleep, wake, think, speak, answer, interrupt, add-on, pause, laugh, question, breathe and move about at adjustable and appropriate speeds, in controlled rhythms. Heart beats are timed based on one's level of activity and internal oxygen levels/needs. The lungs are timed as well for normal activity, slumber and different degrees of hard work. Kidneys function at a certain speed as does growth. Food is moved, degraded and passed along with timing.

The brain is the ultimate organizer. It actually does much more work while we're asleep than while we're awake. It's rewiring itself, making new connections, modifying others, probably reviewing the day and selecting what it wants to keep and what needs discarding. Insomnia or less downtime, we know, impacts creative thinking. Those "all-nighters" that students pull to cram for exams have very limited value. In fact, several studies suggest there's a minus value. If one truly misses sleep for several days, their health can be severely impacted. Somehow, continued sleep deprivation is associated with death. The reason is not clear, but studies on rats[125] have shown certain hormones like cortisol and thyroid drop off, later glucose(sugar) metabolism is altered, temperature drops, and the immune system becomes suppressed.

The brain does many interesting things. One that intrigues me is transient global amnesia (TGA) or the temporary loss of memory that lacks an explanation other than purposeful design. I believe it's a protective measure of going blank when attacked or seriously injured—to blot out intense fear and excruciating pain. Adding to this, life systems try to lessen pain and fear. Most predators seem to know to go for the neck, for that quick kill. Designed or accidental?

I recall a bicyclist who was T-boned on his way to work and in the hospital ICU with severe injuries for several weeks. The only thing he remembered was leaving home that morning. I had a fisherman from a Russian trawler who was severely injured when trapped in a huge, incoming net. He couldn't recall anything from that day. I've cared for victims of violent crimes, including rape, who have no recollection of the attack. Not all, unfortunately. TGA can follow emotional trauma. It seems to be a built-in design.

Another interesting function that is hard to explain is sleep paralysis. That's the paralysis that keeps us safely still during sleep.

---

125 https://slate.com/news-and-politics/2009/05/can-you-die-from-lack-of-sleep.html

This is something more than just for relaxation. Common sense suggests it's there to prevent injuries when we might be acting out our dreams. That's speculation, however, as the phenomenon is not well explained.

Recall a moment when you dreamed you were running in your sleep, to get away from something awful, yet your legs wouldn't work? They were incredibly heavy. Or, you were dreaming you needed to scream out for help, but you couldn't make a sound? Your mouth might open, but no shout followed. You were mute. I believe all this (and some) is sleep paralysis at work. Yet, our subconscious protector knows when to relent to allow a person to move or roll over, to prevent muscle damage and bedsores. Imagine how nighttime in your neighborhood might be if we all acted out our dreams. If it weren't so dangerous, it might be funny.

Proof of sleep paralysis can be seen in the rare person who remains paralyzed for several seconds after waking. This can be very frightening, but, as far as we can tell, breathing remains intact as does heart and other organ functions. One just cannot move.

Faulty mechanisms with sleep paralysis results in the kicking or punching of partners, sleepwalking, and some night terrors. Note some defendants use sleep walking as a defense. In London (2008), Bryan Thomas was found not guilty of killing his wife. He claimed to be fighting off an intruder in his sleep and strangled his wife. He had a long history of sleepwalking.

There are numerous instances where a sleeping person has slugged, even beaten up, their bed-partner. I've seen films of a man who got his wife in a tight headlock, even though she is screaming for him to stop. He claimed he thought he had a deer in hand. People have dived off beds, incurring serious injuries, dreaming that they were on a diving board or jumping from a plane. There was a young teenager, known for sleepwalking, who quickly walked through her parents' bedroom in the middle of the night, went out on the balcony and, despite their screams, jumped two stories. She woke with both legs fractured.

Without sleep paralysis we might all be acting out our dreams every night, injuring ourselves and others. Like everything in life, this mechanism is not perfect. Maybe some of us have damaged it with medications or industrial pollution. I don't know. Fortunately, in the vast majority of instances, the paralysis will turn off the instant one awakes. It's so quick, you don't realize it was in effect. It's the same for eyes. They roll up as you close your eyes (presumably to protect them) and roll back into place as you open them. But, you wouldn't know it.

The more important question might be what really is sleep. Superficially, that may seem like a dumb question, but it's not really fatigue-related. How many times have you seen a marathon runner take a nap immediately after completing the 26.2 mile course? Probably none, because sleep, even though we say we're tired, has nothing to do with being tired. Note how much a newborn sleeps, yet a one or two-week old does little more than wake for feeding, pooping and peeing.

"Science cannot explain why something, rather than nothing, exists."

DENNIS PRAGER, RADIO HOST AND TORAH SCHOLAR

Final Thoughts

D ennis Prager raises a very interesting point in his book *Genesis: God, Creation and Destruction*[126]. He says: "The compelling rational argument is, as noted, is the question **'Why is there anything?'** Science and atheism have no answer to this "anything" question. Nor will they ever. It is outside their purview. Science easily explains what is, but, it cannot explain why what came about—why something, rather than nothing, exists. Only an Intelligent Designer of that something can explain why."

In part, I have attempted to show the major differences between Intelligent Design and the theory of evolution. I have braided these throughout the book in effort to see where we might be going and how. I have tried to show what has worked and what hasn't. Herein is a new (yet, really old) destiny. **Just as we were Designed for many purposes, such as glorifying God, pursuing happiness, raising a family and maintaining dominion over the Earth, might we be designing our stand-in for activities we can never do?** Will a human or a humanoid plant a flag on the first exoplanet to be explored? My money's on the latter.

We are clearly on track to create many facsimiles of ourselves; they will surely improve with time. All relevant technologies are converging. They were discussed herein, from robotic walking to talking and from artificial seeing to thinking (AI). Little did the first person, millennia ago, know that a jagged piece of magnifying glass was the beginning of a new "race".

Can we ever make a human being? A real human being? I don't think it's possible even if given another billion years to do so. That is partly due to the complexity upon complexity of the many convergent designs and the fact that trillions of macroscopic and microscopic parts that would need to be duplicated and made to work

---

126 Dennis Prager. Genesis: *God, Creation and Destruction*, as part of the Rational Bible series (Regnery Faith, 2019) 3.

together. **But, my opinion is mostly based on the inability to define and copy that intangible spark of life that gives man his spirit and soul.**

With rare exceptions, we all desire more and more creature comforts, less time working, more free time to play and less drudgery. Robots and humanoids will definitely help make much of that happen. At what price, however? They will get better and better at what they do and what they can replace. Humanoid forerunners are already here. You probably spoke to at least one today. Another may take your job tomorrow. They can be found in coffee shops, bars, kitchens and department stores. The International Space Station already has one.

We may reach a point when humanoids will not be easily distinguished from DNA-based people. To know, with certainty, that you are dealing with a faux person, you may have to feel for a pulse in their wrist or press on their neck. Real people may not appreciate the latter, especially if it happens unannounced. Or, do a finger pinprick to see if they bleed real blood. This is not the best greeting to give a friendly neighbor who simply came to borrow a rake. As a last resort, if you can carry a thermometer, you might check the individual's temperature. Robots will surely have ambient temperatures. All these are unlikely approaches.

If you're still not sure, one could challenge it with the Turing test or Winograd Schema Challenge. Try a sarcastic joke to see if it laughs at the right time and in the right way. Laughing too short or too long might be a clue. Laughing plus coughing or tearing up might be revealing. Note humanoids are not likely to show sincere empathy, sympathy, kindness, compassion or our type of curiosity. Challenge them with what-if examples. Or, give them an Amelia Bedelia test such as asking them to put dates in the cake or to dust the furniture.

Man has always wanted to travel to the distant heavens (one of our purposes), but that will mostly happen by proxy. The further away the galaxy, the less likely humans can make the journey. Some of the present day astronauts have shown "space brain", meaning cognitive changes (damages) from cosmic radiation. And, that's up there for a relatively short duration. Very few astronauts can walk on their own when they first return. Height can even change as the vertebrae spread out; this lends itself to severe, chronic back pain.

Humans cannot, given today's technology, live long enough for a roundtrip, sleep for decades, and/or safely breed to reach the nearest stars. Having procreation to create future generations en route is presently a pipe-dream. Is there a danger to a pregnant woman and her unborn out there? Given the problem of "space brain", the answer is a very likely yes. Just providing enough food and oxygen for the sojourn appears to be a near-impossible task. Robots don't need to eat. And, they don't need to breathe.

Wanderlust and exploring the nearest galaxies seems to be ingrained in our genes—essentially, to go where man has never gone before—much as it once was for trekking across the Bering land bridge, riding along the Silk Road to China, circumnavigating the oceans of the world, and piloting Apollo 11 to the moon. Some of us would like to climb the highest mountains, dive to the to the Mariana Trench, and explore the longest, darkest caves. We cannot help ourselves.

What sane person(s), however is going to volunteer to go on a decades-long journey to a distant galaxy without any guarantee of coming home? Who's going to undertake a trial of suspended animation (once invented) here on Earth for a five or ten years to see if it works? No one on this side of insanity. Not me. None of these problems will change until we can travel faster than light, if that is even possible, and/or discover shortcuts such as wormholes. So far, travels such as these, short of robots, are science fiction.

Suppose deep space journeys will never be safe for human beings[127], should we send human lookalikes (faux people)? Or, just

---

127 "Astronauts have to breathe, eat, drink, and keep their demons at bay. Robots fly free of such constraints. They can do more, go more places, and because they don't

hang it up? If we simply settle for radioing messages (SETI style), extraterrestrials may not know how to receive or download them. They may not even be able to find/hear them. Arriving as human-oids might help enormously, especially if the aliens turn out to be human beings. But, what if these ET's were Neanderthals? Properly programmed humanoids might be able to find a way to communi-cate with them, for whatever that is worth. That is, if they even come out from hiding.

Space travel is no longer elective, more so imperative, pressed on by international competition, space wars, treasures like precious metals, and possibly a need for species-perpetuation. Robots will have to build habitats in advance of astronauts coming (and staying). Whoever owns the moon and/or Mars may control human destiny.

The ultimate human race is on.

A need may come to escape Earth. Aspects of our living spaces are being choked by industrial pollution, and our seas are dying from micro-plastics, poachers and over-fishing. Many fish and other sea life carry our antibiotics and other drugs like female hormones, antide-pressants and blood pressure meds. Old plagues, may be returning. Pathological bacteria are becoming more resistant to antibiotics and viruses may resurface like the infamous Spanish flu that killed tens of millions. Food chains are being altered by massive extinctions. Climate seems to be changing for the worse. And, weapons are becoming even more destructive. We could easily annihilate all life with the next war or nuclear accident. We do not as yet have a good defense for an aster-oid direct hit. They can happen virtually any time. And, try to project our future with the problem of dwindling sperm counts which might be due to our medications, female hormones in our water, microwaves from phones and/or pollution. We don't know. We may be left with

---

require life support systems, they are thus cheaper than human missions—do it all more often.", attributed to Howard McCurdy, American University Public Policy pro-fessor and co-author of *Robots in Space.*

cloning (only) to continue the human race, until the last batch of frozen sperm has been used or the "Use Before" date has been passed. The clock is "ticking" on so many issues.

We like ourselves way too much not to want to re-create ourselves. Our fascination with I, Me, and Myself can be traced back to pre-historic times, Why not have a little me, elsewhere? Or, a bunch of little me's everywhere? If I consider myself brilliant (and wealthy) beyond all others, the world needs more of me, right? Jeffrey Epstein thought so. Note the epidemic of selfies and the success of industry giants such as FaceBook and Twitter that capitalize on narcissism. Listen in on virtually any conversation. Some of us fall in love with ourselves.

We are on a path of substituting mechanical beings in virtually every activity man does. Computers can already write short stories, paint sceneries, and compose music. Hardly a human activity has ever been discovered or invented that somebody else hasn't come along with a way to set up a competition and make it bigger, faster, smaller, trickier. If your robot can do two cartwheels and a back-flip, ours will do three cartwheels, two back flips and recite poetry, all at the same time. We have beauty contests starting with newborns. Centenarians are lining up to run the 100 yard dash. We clock races down to the hundredth of a second. That will eventually go to the thousandth. Weight-lifting may have to go to pounds plus ounces. Humanoids will probably do all this too.

Herein, I have also attempted to use the theories of evolution and Intelligent Design to explain our possible origins and tie them into a timeline and a specific purpose that I sense, that is driving us to re-create man. I also believe understanding humanoid design helps to understand Intelligent Design. Anyone who supports the theory of evolution (only) must explain obvious biological foresight and planning, the different convergences of complexity upon complexity, in the animal and plant world and the presence of a different soul in each human being.

If we are here on Earth simply by an incredible series (billions, if not more) of accidents and not created by an Intelligent Designer, one might say we cannot have a purpose. That means a person's purpose is whatever he or she deems it. Or, what the ultimate boss demands, be that a President, a dictator or the toughest guy on the block. And, if he/she forces us to comply? If there's no true purpose(s), there's no reason to have religion, synagogues, churches and mosques. Maybe then, there's no need for ethics, morals and manners.

The problems with the theory of evolution have been enumerated in many texts[128]. The gaps between species are getting wider and wider. **They need a God of the Gaps and don't know it. Or, won't admit it.** For me, convergences of design upon converges of design, working in tandem, in parallel and serially, without foresight and planning, not only boggles the mind, it also demolishes the tenets of the theory of evolution. Perhaps one could speculate Intelligence Guidance (God of the Gaps) connecting the links in the bracelets. Granted natural selection can create horses that can run faster (up to a point), octopuses with better camouflage (within reason), and the rabbit that can reproduce more offspring (if mechanically possible) to improve survival, **but no one has ever shown that one species can change into another. The genetic changes that are needed are way too complicated and overwhelmingly numerous.** Random, unexplained, beneficial changes such as mutations are rare if they even exist. Mutations are almost always negligible or seriously damaging. **Most important, evolution cannot explain the spark of life. And, Lightning Kills!** Shocking a collection of amino acids in a primordial soup did not spawn life. Every species evolving into man requires way too many complex, convoluted steps to make the evolutionary jumps.

And, who is talking to whom when you are speaking to yourself? Is the kinder voice coming from your soul? And/or, the devil

---

128 See recommended reading list at the end of this book.

deep within? Can all this dialogue be explained by a series of yet-undiscovered algorithms? Some folks say there's a committee meeting going on in their head. You only think that you think? That is, I think I think, I think. Are we all being fooled? Note C.S. Lewis[129] once said: "You don't have a soul. You are a soul. You have a body."

Many aspects of our design seem ideal. Planning/Foresight placed cutting teeth in the front of the mouth and flat grinders in back. Intake of food high, by products out low. Bones have a way of healing themselves, in case they break. Blood vessels have a way of healing an injury, in case you bleed. The nose is always above the mouth, not below, fingernails are on the outside, not the inside, and the brain is securely tucked inside a bony barrier.

Apologies for repetition, but **I consider this a very strong argument against evolution: Our spinal cord is twisted 180 degrees (halves change sides). There is no obvious benefit fit in the evolution model. Yet, our spinal cord is braided or twisted. Half of each optic nerve (about 400,000 nerve fibers) crossover to the opposite eye. The inner or nasal aspect of the left eye is innervated by the right brain and the inner or nasal aspect of the right eye is innervated by the left brain. There is no apparent evolutionary (survival) benefit here, also.** One might speculate that vision is so important that right and left brain needed to view through both sides. Or, could this be Foresight, i.e., in case one ehe is blinded, both sides of the brain will still get survival information? **If the spinal cord were to simply roll over, the nerves to the eyes ought not be, cannot be, split in half. And, the spinal side-changing doesn't stop there. In some ways it looks like challah bread. There is no apparent way any of this happened by a succession of small steps. It would take millions. The theory of evolution would definitely need a God of the Gaps here. Maybe, the same God as Intelligent Designer.**

---

129 Clive Staples Lewis was a British writer and theologian best known for *The Chronicles of Narnia* and non-fiction Christian apologetics.

We have opposing thumbs, mirror-imaged hands, doubled sensory (two eyes, two ears, two nostrils that are spaced appropriately for distance and depth perception), organs for spatial determinations, hands to catch your fall or a falling branch or a caveman's club, pheromones to make procreation desirable, very compatible genitalia, and an extremely complex brain to direct, control and initiate nearly all of our activities.

There's a what-if cough for material that accidentally slips into the trachea, vomiting for noxious foods, a sneeze to rid irritants in the nose, diarrhea to eliminate infections from the intestines and hiccups to dislodge food that is stuck in the esophagus. A fever is present to kill microscopic invaders with heat. The (D)designer had to know these problems might arise and created them in advance, just in case. This **what-if list,** especially when it gets into the microscopic, submicroscopic and chemical realms, becomes enormous. There are systems to control water and salt intakes, gas exchanges, blood pressure, heart rates and hormones as well as protection against excesses and deficiencies of minerals, vitamins and nutrients. Fight, flight or freeze are inside all of us for many what-if emergencies.

We have an immune system that is capable of making a variety of antibodies—this is without knowing, in advance, what the likely, or never before seen, infecting agents would be and/or how it can be destroyed. We had a variety of specific enzymes in our saliva and gut long before these juices were exposed to tacos, and turkey meatloaf. There's pH-controlling mucous to protect the stomach from its own acid. We have skin to keep us moist and control our internal temperature. Why have a back-up, pacing system in the heart? Why have a clotting system in advance? It's important to point out again that a newborn baby take its very first breath **immediately** after delivery, rather than before or too late? Seconds literally count. This clearly shows Planning. Any number of errors can deny a species existence.

It should be apparent that the precise creation of a true human being by scientists (other human beings), I believe, will be forever impossible. And, I suspect, forever unnecessary. **Just studying the different processes recorded herein, one should realize that our bodies and our minds are way too complex to have come about by chance or accident, meaning evolution, no matter how fortuitous the accidents.** The vast majority of structures and processes cannot be created on their own. The information systems cannot spontaneously show up and add on. They require an Intelligent Designer. If there are no Intelligent Purposes, then why are we here? It appears as if our design will be carried across the universe.

This book did not write itself. Nor, did the Book of Life write itself.

Every painting must have a painter.
Every poem must have a poet.
Every statue must have a sculptor.
Every blueprint must have an architect.
Every building must have a builder.
Every book must have an author.
Every meal must have a cook.
Every child must have a parent.
Every class must have a teacher.
Every masterpiece must have a master.
Every code must have a coder.
Every program must have a programmer.
Every zoo must have a zookeeper.
Every formula must have a mathematician
Every plan must have a planner.
Every design must have a designer.
Every creation must have a Creator.

"For believers there are no questions; for non-believers there are no answers."

CHOFETZ CHAIM (1839-1933) , RABBINIC AND TALMUDIC SCHOLAR

Recommended Reading

Alexander Tsiaras. *From Conception to Birth: A life Unfolds* (Doubleday, 2002).

Ben Russell(editor). *Robots: The 500-Year Quest to Make Machines Human* (Scala Arts & Heritage Publishers, Ltd. 2017).

Charles Darwin. The Origin Of Species (Bantam Classics, 1999)

Benjamin Wiker and Jonathan Witt. *A Meaningful World: How the Arts and Sciences Reveal the Genius of Nature*(IVP Academic, 2006).

Charles Tanford & Jacqueline Reynolds. *Nature's Robots: a History of Proteins* (Oxford University Press, 2001).

Clive D. L. Wynne. *Do Animals Think?* (Princeton University Press, 2006).

Dennis Prager. *Genesis: God, Creation and Destruction*, as part of the Rational Bible series (Regnery Faith, 2019).

Despina Kakoudaki. *Anatomy of a Robot: Literature, Cinema, and Cultural Work of Artificial People* (Rutgers University Press, 2014).

Douglas Axe. *Undeniable: How Biology Confirms Our Intuition That Life is Designed*(HarperOne, 2017)

Douglas Erwin and James Valentine. *The Cambrian Explosion* (W. H. Freeman, 2013).

Edward Steele, et al. *Lamarck's Signature: How Retrogenics Are Changing Darwin's Natural Selection Paradigm* (Perseus Books, 1998)

Emily Anthes. *Frankenstein's Cat: Cuddling Up To Biotech's Brave New Beasts*. Scientific American (Farrar, Straus and Giroux, 2013).

Francis Hitching. *The Neck of the Giraffe: Or Where Darwin Went Wrong*(Ticknor&Fields, 1982).

George G. Bridgnan. *The Human Machine: The Anatomical Structure and Mechanism of the Human Body*(Dover Publications, 1972).

Gerald L. Schroder. *The Science of God: The Convergence of Scientific and Biblical Wisdom*(Free Press, 2007).

Gregory Berns. *What's It Like to Be a Dog: And Other Adventures in Animal Neuroscience* (Basic Books, 2017).

Guillermo Gonzalez and Jay Richards. *The Privileged Planet: How Our Place In The Cosmos Is Designed For Discovery* (Regnery Publishing, Inc., 2004).

Jerry Kaplan. *Artificial Intelligence: What Everyone Needs to Know* (Oxford University Press, 2014).

Jonathan Wells. *The Icons of Evolution*(Regnery Publishing, 2002) *Zombie Science*(Discovery Institute, 2017).

Kai-Fu Lee. *AI Super-Powers: China, Silicon and the New World Order* (Houghton, Mifflin Harcourt, 2018).

Karl Williams. *Build Your Own Humanoid Robots* (McGraw-Hill, 2004).

Marcos Eberlin. *Foresight: How the Chemistry of Life Reveals Planning and Purpose* (Discovery Institute Press, 2019).

Michael J. Behe. *Darwin's Black Box* (Free Press, 2006)
  Darwin Devolves (HarperOne, 2019)
  The Edge of Evolution: The Search for the Limits of Darwinism (Free Press, 2007).

Peter Godfrey-Smith. *Other Minds: The Octopus, The Sea and The Deep Origins of Consciousness (Farrar, Strauss and Giroux, Reprint 2017).*

Phillip E. Johnson. *Darwin on Trial* (IVP Books; 20th Anniversary edition, October 5, 2010).

Ray Kurzweil. *The Singularity is Near: When Humans Transcend Biology* (Viking Press 2005).

Richard Dawkins. *The Blind Watchmaker (W.W.Norton, 2015)*
  The Selfish Gene (Oxford Press 2016)
  The God Delusion (Mariner Books, 2008)

Richard Sole and Brian Goodwin. *Signs of Life: How Complexity Pervades Biology* (Basic Books,2000).

Richard Ellis. *Aquagenesis: The Origin and Evolution of Life in the Sea* (Viking adult, 2003).

Roger D. Launius and Howard E. McCurdy *Robots in Space* (John Hopkins University Press, 2008).

Stephen Jay Gould. *The Panda's Thumb* (W.W. Norton & Company, Reissue edition, 1992).

Stephen Meyer. *Signature in the Cell*(HarperOne,(August 20,2010)

Geoffrey Simmons, M.D.

Darwin's Doubt(HarperOne,2014)
The Return of the God Hypothesis (HarperOne, 2019).

William Dembski *The Design of Life: Discovering Signs of of Intelligence in Biological Systems* (ISI Distributed Titles, 2005)
The Design Revolution (Intervarsity Press, 2004).

William Paley. *Natural Theology* (Benediction Classics 2017).

Made in the USA
Middletown, DE
22 November 2019

79200457R00184